Deep Well

DEEP WELL

by Emil Paul John

ILLUSTRATED BY AL NAGY

FRIENDSHIP PRESS · NEW YORK

In the United States, Parent-Teachers' Associations are so well established most people simply call them PTAs. Nowhere in the world are parents and teachers so organized in their efforts to influence children as in the United States; yet American children waver on the path toward respect for these same parents and teachers.

There are no organized PTAs in many parts of the world, but people everywhere realize the important influence parents and teachers exert upon children. When my own parents were growing up in the mountains of Turkey, the thing they feared most was bringing grief to their parents and teachers.

To them, my personal PTA, I dedicate this book—perhaps because I still have one foot in the "old country," perhaps because I was blessed by having real parents and real teachers. I hope that *Deep Well* will bring them no grief, and that the stories will help clear away some of the obstacles our own children face on that path toward respect.

EMIL PAUL JOHN

Contents

INTRODUCTION 11

1 THE PRISONERS 25

2 WORK CAMP 49

3 FLOWER 75

4 DRIVE-IN DESERT 97

5 THE APPLES 125

CONCLUSION 157

Introduction

IT TOOK MY FATHER TWENTY-FIVE YEARS TO ADMIT that he was afraid of the Turks. I received his letter at Christmastime, 1954, just a few days before I was to leave Vienna for Istanbul.

"Listen to me, my son," he wrote, "travel if you must, but do not go to Turkey. You are a Christian, and no Christian is welcome in that country."

Both my father and mother had sad memories of the "old country"—memories that they had never shared with their children. The Turkish massacres of Assyrian, Armenian and Greek Christians formed a chapter in their lives that they preferred to forget. My impending visit to Turkey roused long-forgotten images of midnight mobs, of looted homes, of bloody knives, of screaming women and orphaned children.

11

Father accepted my trip reluctantly, and then only after I explained that I was going simply to visit my mother's sister, who had remained in Turkey when the others fled.

Almost a decade later, he found it even more difficult to accept my assignment as a Christian missionary to Algeria.

"Who lives in Algeria?" he asked.

"Mostly Muslims," I replied.

"And you will try to convert them!" He shook his head disbelievingly. "No Muslim has ever been converted to Christianity. In their eyes you will be an unbeliever. Why would you want to go there?"

I was being sent (one of several hundred "relief workers") to help bind the wounds caused by seven years of war. Many of these workers were sent by the church in the belief that Christian charity ought to be extended to everyone according to his need, not according to his religion. I answered my father's question with a question of my own: "Aren't we all human beings?"

Midway through my assignment, I was commissioned to reopen an abandoned mission station located in the Atlas Mountains. During the fighting the station had been used as a base by French soldiers holding off the Algerian guerrillas. The church wanted to convert one of the buildings to a hospital, and it was my job to utilize local labor and materials. Fortunately for me a nearby

Muslim village supplied a goodly number of skilled masons, carpenters and painters who had worked in France. But the only good plumber lived fifteen miles down the valley. Each morning I had to drive to his village to pick him up; each evening I had to drive him home.

The plumber's name was Akli. Although he had worked in France for fifteen years, spoke French and wore European-style clothes, he remained faithful to his Muslim religion. His only wish was to spend the rest of his days in these mountains and valleys with his family—his mother, wife and six children.

Many mornings as I drove the valley road I passed a short, barefoot, bearded old man who carried a stick. He looked so like old Ben Gunn—right out of the pages of *Treasure Island*—that I promptly dubbed him that in my mind. Even his gait rivaled that of Ben and his mountain-goat companions.

My curiosity was roused, but the villagers told me little: old "Ben" was mentally ill and did nothing but walk (or more accurately—lope) the valley road, sometimes covering as much as thirty miles a day. Each time I saw his small figure, sympathy stirred within me; I wanted to help him. Often I said to myself, "If I had powers of healing, I would stop right now, touch this old man and make him whole!"

One day I asked the plumber about "Ben."

"This 'crazy fool' was once the most brilliant teacher and scholar in this region. He spoke Arabic so beautifully that people came from distant villages to listen to him. But these qualities also aroused envy and jealousy among other teachers. In an effort to eliminate this rival, one of the teachers put poison into his drink. The scholar drank, became unconscious and appeared to be dead.

"As is the custom here," the plumber went on, "the 'dead' man was buried immediately—in a shallow grave, as is also the custom. It was fortunate that only about a foot of loose earth covered the shrouded body, for the effects of the poison wore off, and the teacher revived. Imagine finding yourself buried alive! The man was strong despite his small size, and, by exerting a tremendous effort, he managed to dig himself out. No one knows whether the shock of awakening inside a grave or the effects of the poison caused the change—he has never been the same. He walks the valley road at a furious pace from sunrise to sunset—sometimes even under the stars. He stops only to pick up scraps of food that are thrown to him and to sleep under bushes along the roadside. As far as I know, he has never changed his clothes since that unfortunate incident many years ago."

His tale finished, the plumber added that, in his opinion, the man was "off his rocker" but perfectly harmless.

"Often I meet him in town and talk with him," Akli added. "He is so gentle that even when children laugh at him and throw sticks at him—as, I am ashamed to say, they do—he never strikes back, nor have I ever seen him become angry at them. Although my own income is barely enough to feed my family, I try to give him a franc now and then, for which he is always pathetically grateful."

This gruesome story increased my desire to help the unfortunate creature. Now when I passed "Ben" on the road, I uttered impassioned prayers; I asked God to cleanse him of this "demon" which had entered him certainly through no fault of his own. But I never stopped to talk to him—was there no time? Or was I uncertain about how to speak to such a person?

The day of my final journey to Akli's village was a sad one for both the plumber and me. We were of different religions; he was a plumber and I a sort of white-collar worker, yet the bond that had grown between us was very like that between brothers.

Alki expressed, as he had often done before, his admiration for the relief workers in his country. "It was hard enough for me to imagine," he said, "that anyone from one nation would help someone in another. That one should also be a Christian, and the other a Muslim, that one would cross an ocean to assist another of a different race—*that* is beyond my comprehension!"

Then Akli lifted his hands before him, raised his eyes upward and prayed, "God grant that someday, if I am ever the possessor of riches, I too may be kind to others."

We were still on the valley road when the figure of the bearded man appeared in the distance. I said to the plumber, "There's our little friend." Akli laughed. We soon caught up to him, but just as we were about to pass I slammed my foot on the brake.

"Something wrong?" the plumber asked.

"Find out where he's going," I replied. "Maybe we can give him a ride."

The old man said he was going to the village near the mission hospital and accepted our offer gratefully. He climbed in and sat cross-legged on the floor—the seats had been removed so we could carry more supplies. I glanced at him as we started off, and he laughed softly, but did not speak.

We traveled another mile on the valley road, then turned up the mountain trail winding to the hospital. Akli remarked to me that it was odd that the old man should be going to the village. He had never been there before, nor had he ever walked off the valley road. "Why don't you ask him?" I replied. Akli did so, but "Ben" just shrugged and pointed to the top of the mountain.

"What will you do there?" I asked.

"I will turn around and walk back down," the old man replied.

I considered the strange circumstances of this meeting —had "God himself" arranged for this man to be in my bus on my final day in Algeria? Perhaps now it would be possible for me to place my hand upon his head and bless him! Even if I had no power of healing, at least I could communicate to him by touch and by facial expression my wish for God's blessing upon him. And who knows what "miracle" God might work! If my faith isn't strong enough to "move this mountain," I thought, then I will drive him directly to the mission hospital, and he can be the first patient. Maybe his sickness isn't mental; maybe an operation could restore him to his former self!

Even as these lofty thoughts surged through my mind, I became aware of a strange odor. Had I run over a skunk? Was it a freshly fertilized field? But there was nothing fresh about this odor! It was so penetrating that I concentrated all my attention on getting rid of it. First I closed the windows, then I opened them wide, but the smell persisted. Finally I asked the plumber what it could be. Akli smiled and discreetly pointed his finger in the direction of our passenger.

For the remainder of the journey, any thoughts about a miraculous cure for the bearded man were completely routed by my nausea. As soon as we hit the village, I stopped quickly to let him out; I forced myself to smile. He offered his hand; I hesitated, but managed to extend my own. Our hands touched—instead of blessing him I was absorbed by fear that somehow his smell might rub off on me!

The plumber opened the door, and "Ben" jumped to the ground. He waved to me and smiled, then turned and started down the trail. Akli shouted something, took a franc from his pocket, ran after the old man and pressed the coin into his hand.

I watched as if I were paralyzed.

The old man bowed, nodded his thanks and continued down the trail while children of the village streamed out of their houses to throw sticks at him.

I parked on the hospital grounds and opened the car doors wide, to wipe away the traces of this "brother in Christ."

That night a "Christian" missionary—ready to risk life and limb to bring the message of Christ to the "heathen" of North Africa, and glowing with pride over building a hospital for unfortunate people—bade farewell to an ignorant Muslim plumber who didn't know enough to save his meager income to feed his own children!

My father was right. I didn't convert any Muslims to Christianity. On the contrary, after this experience many uncertainties arose in me. If Christ's teaching is to "love one another," then in this case who was Christian?

It was a dilemma. I had grown up with the conviction

18

that there is something supreme and unique about Jesus Christ; how had a simple Muslim been able to act more in accordance with his teaching than I, who represented him? I was certain that the well of Christianity contained the purest water, yet another well had appeared, and the man who drank from it seemed more refreshed than I.

These thoughts hammered louder than the engines of the plane bearing my family and me from Algeria. We stopped over in Tunisia, another of the Muslim nations that line the coast of North Africa, and there an answer was given to me by another simple worker, a tinsmith—only this time he was a follower of the Christian religion.

He was an Armenian who, like my father, had fled from Turkey during the massacres. Why he chose to settle in another Muslim land, while most of his fellow Armenians sought refuge in Europe and America, remains a puzzle. Curiosity about a Christian, who had lived in peace with his Muslim neighbors for so many years, led me to his shop in the heart of Tunis' Arab quarter.

It was obvious that the tinsmith was beloved by his neighbors. Every passerby greeted him with a gesture or salutation of love and goodwill. Even a stranger unfamiliar with the language and people could feel the sincerity of these greetings.

The tinsmith invited me to his home, and I told him about my experiences in Algeria and my uncer-

19

tainties about a Christian's mission in a Muslim land. He seemed to understand perfectly. When he answered, his voice was kind.

"Many years ago, while I was polishing a copper kettle in my shop, I heard noises from the street. I hurried out and saw an angry crowd gathered around two American missionaries who were standing on the corner. The two spoke Arabic fluently and were urging the Muslims to abandon their false religion and to be baptized in the name of the only true Lord and Savior, Jesus Christ. I missed much of what they said but the Muslims obviously didn't like it. They waved their fists and shouted angrily at the Americans. When some stooped to pick up stones I decided it was time to step in. I placed myself in front of the missionaries and cried out to the crowd, 'Do not harm these men! Can't you see that they are mentally ill?' I pulled the Americans inside and advised them to leave the city and never return if they valued their lives."

The tinsmith paused.

"I am not against preaching the gospel," he continued. "I have been a Christian all my life and have remained steadfast in my faith even though I have lived among non-Christians since my childhood. Once I too had the same enthusiasm as American missionaries, but it was my destiny to find other means of spreading the gospel."

I asked the tinsmith why the Muslims loved him as they so obviously did. He seemed surprised at such a simple question, as if I had asked, "How much is two and two?"

"They love me," he replied, "because I am a Christian. I have tried to live as a Christian even in the smallest matters. No man has ever left my shop with hatred toward me. Sometimes a Muslim woman may not have enough money to pay for the kettle she orders. I give it to her anyway, and she pays when she can. In the evening, when all the other shops are closed, and the owners are in the city entertaining themselves with their profits, the light in my shop still burns. Under it you will find me teaching the apprentice boys how to read and write. I do not remember how many I have taught in my forty years here, but all of them became master tinsmiths. Now they have shops of their own. If they needed money to start, I advanced it to them.

"How often my fellow Christians have called me a fool, and how often I have been tempted to agree with them! But a few years ago there was a great riot in Tunis."

The tinsmith hesitated as if he were uncertain. He poured me another cup of coffee, took a sip from his own cup, and looked steadily into my eyes. Finally he smiled and proceeded:

"Because you have made the effort to come to me, I

will tell you about the riot; you may also find an answer to some of the questions that seem to bother you.

"Military action by the French at a nearby naval base began the riots. Many Muslims retaliated by beating any foreigners they could find; they burned and looted shops. I barricaded myself inside my shop. I could hear them coming, and I shivered as I remembered a similar night, long ago in Turkey. I was prepared for the end as the mob beat upon my door. Suddenly the rioters stopped.

"My Muslim neighbors were challenging the mob. A voice shouted, 'Do not touch that shop. Yes, indeed, the tinsmith *is* a Christian, but he is worth ten of us!' "

The tinsmith sighed—it was evident he was reliving that night. I sat in respectful silence. After a moment he roused, shook his head as if to clear it, and concluded:

"Your two American missionaries attempted to preach the gospel and aroused only antagonism in those who heard them. But a simple tinsmith, trying to live according to the Lord's commandments, brought out the best in man. I know the one who shouted. He is a devout Muslim. But do you doubt that Jesus Christ was alive in him when he risked his life to defend me?

"As for your own uncertainties about which religion is best or, as you expressed it, 'which well contains the purest water,' I advise you to put aside such questions. The answers mean nothing. What matters is that you learn to drink from your own well."

1   The Prisoners

THE GUARD STUCK HIS HEAD IN THE DOOR OF THE small anteroom and looked at the prisoners awaiting arraignment.

"You intend to sing them songs?" he asked.

"What songs?"

"I don't know what you call 'em. But seems like every bunch we get in here lately has gotta' sing."

"Any law against it?"

"Nope, no law," he grinned. "But you better have prettier voices than the last ones!"

The guard pointed at one of the prisoners—a bronze-skinned Negro. "If he gives you trouble, just yell; I'll be right here."

The four looked guardedly at each other—a white man who had answered the guard's questions, a white girl neatly dressed in skirt and sweater, and two Negroes in their early twenties, maybe younger. One Negro's skin was bronze, the other's, black.

"Well . . . if we've got to be birds in the same cage," the girl said nervously, "we might as well know each other. My name is Florence Chadburn."

"There's nothing to fear, Florence," the white man soothed her. "We'll be out of here in an hour."

"Oh, Mr. Minor," she replied, "I'm not worried a bit. This is the most wonderful thing that's ever happened to me. I feel as if I'm really doing something worthwhile."

"This is Mr. Minor, he's a minister. . . ." She dwindled off. The white man stood and offered his hand, but no one took it.

"Brown—that's my name," said the dark Negro, and added almost with a sneer, "They call me Bomber —like they used to call Joe Louis 'The Brown Bomber' —me, I'm Bomber Brown."

Florence paused to give the other Negro a chance to introduce himself, but everything about him, except his eyes, remained still.

"Are you all right?" Mr. Minor asked Bomber. "What happened? You were behind me and the next thing I knew, you were wrestling on the ground." He tried to inspect the bruise on the man's cheek, but Bomber pulled away in anger.

"Keep your dirty hands off me," Brown snarled. He

mopped ineffectually at the bruise with his handkerchief and turned to the other Negro, who stood in a
corner of the cell like a cigar-store Indian. "You better
have a good reason for what you did out there, 'cause if
you don't, I'm gonna make you wish you was in soli-
tary!"

"Cut it out!"—Mr. Minor stepped quickly between
the Negroes— "Any foolishness and I'll call for the
guard!"

"So, one of those turn-the-other-cheekers," Brown
simpered. "I know, I trained for that, too. Swallow everythin' they throw at you. Smile back. Chin up. Don't
even think mad. Listen to me, man, I can take anythin' from a white man. I ain't scared no more.
Someday it'll be my turn to crack the whip. But out
there on that picket line, for no reason at all, when one
of my own kind jumps me. . . ."

The other Negro cut in sharply. "I am not your kind!
You are a slave! You are my enemy!"

"Man, are you crazy?"

"Sit down, both of you—sit down!" Mr. Minor ordered.

Three sat down. The aloof stranger continued to stand
alone. No one spoke, yet the cell thundered. The girl was
afraid. Since joining the civil rights movement, she had
seen squabbles among Negroes, but nothing like this.
She glanced at the others and tried to smile.

27

"I want it understood, there'll be no fighting here," Mr. Minor continued. "We don't know who you are, but you're welcome to our cause. When our lawyer arrives, I'll ask him to make arrangements for your release, too."

"I don't need help from a whitey," Brown replied.

"I have done nothing wrong," the unidentified man spoke softly.

"All of us are charged with disturbing the peace," Mr. Minor replied. "Whether we believe our picketing was right will not matter."

"I was not picketing. Whatever your cause, I am not interested in it."

"Our cause is your cause," responded the minister. "We are fighting for equality and freedom for all men in this country. And if anyone should have been in our picket line, it was you. But never mind. If you did attack Mr. Brown, you will be charged the same as we are—only in your case I'd say they had a right to put you in jail."

He glanced at the girl, patted her shoulder, and repeated, "Don't worry, Florence, we'll be out of here in no time."

Florence was confused. How long had she tried to prove to herself and to everyone around her that people of different races can live happily together? In high school and college she had gone out of her way to mingle with Negro students. White students liked her; her attractive appearance and cheerful personality were envied by her classmates, but Florence ignored them. She joined any movement on campus that had in its statement of aims the words "equality" and "freedom."

A white man's prejudice against a Negro was understandable to her, even if it was wrong; but for one Negro to assault another Negro and call him "slave" and "enemy"—how could this be?

"Have you seen him before?" she whispered to Brown.

"Never in my life."

The stranger watched them; he knew they were talking about him, but it didn't bother him. He was more concerned over a gnawing sensation growing in his chest. He knew it well—every time he disappointed someone he loved, this nibbling began. But why now?

The figures in front of him began to blur. A scene from his boyhood started to take shape in his mind. The shadows on the wall shimmering through the latticed windows transported him to a familiar room in Africa. Instead of Mr. Minor, a tall, bearded white man dressed in a white robe sat beside him.

"How did it go last night, Ikomu?" the man asked.

"I whipped them out of the house, Father Peurot," his own voice replied. "Bahutus are barking dogs; filled with wine, they become worse than jackals."

"Did they harm you?"

"What harm can a Bahutu do to a Watusi?" The boy was scornful. "For four hundred years they have been our slaves. If it were not for my father, I would have had them put to death."

"It is fortunate that your father is the king of the Watusis and not his son," Father Peurot remonstrated. Ikomu lowered his eyes; he could not face his teacher's reproach and disappointment.

"You will sit on your father's throne someday. How will you be able to rule over others when you cannot rule yourself?"

"When Bahutus are drunk, they are possessed with devils."

"No, the wine only makes them say what is in their hearts."

"I did not like what they said about my tribe and about my father and me. If I hear them again, I will cut out their tongues!"

The priest walked over to the latticed window and gazed out at the Bahutus laboring in the fields. In the forty years he had served as a missionary to this land, he had worked and dreamed for the day that the Bahutu could stand beside the Watusi as an equal. Only the seated boy could realize his hopes. Ikomu's father cooperated with the priest toward this goal; he was wise enough to know that changes must come. But the king was old, his son must learn to understand that no man can keep another in bondage forever.

The white man sought for the right words. "When the Bahutus became drunk last night"—he hesitated for a moment, then plunged on—"your father and I decided that if you heard their thoughts from their own lips, you might come to understand what you must do."

"I know what they think and it does not bother me."

"But it *did* bother you," Father Peurot said. "You are even ready to cut out their tongues. You consider them your slaves but the opposite is true. *You* are a slave to their feelings about you."

"I am the son of the king! I am no man's slave!"

"Bravo! You speak the truth, Ikomu. The king's son *should* be free. But you are his son in flesh only. When you are able to bear no malice toward any man who speaks ill of you, when you can bless the man who curses you, you will be free. Only then will you be worthy to rule the Watusis and the Bahutus—even all of Africa. Last night you demonstrated that you are unable to control yourself—even toward drunkards who cannot be held responsible for what they say and do."

"I am the son of the king," Ikomu protested. "I am no slave—I am. . . ."

The latticework shifted, the African background faded and he was back in the American prison.

31

Florence, Mr. Minor and Bomber Brown were staring at him.

"Are you all right?" the white man asked. "Why don't you sit down?"

The African sank onto the bench, head in his hands, and for a long moment there was stillness. Then he uncovered his eyes and said, "My name is Ikomu. I am sorry for the way I have behaved."

Florence smiled. It was as if someone had opened the window and let the sunlight in.

"Forget it," Mr. Minor replied. "We all lose our temper now and then."

"Where are you from?" the girl asked.

"East Africa."

"Are you a student?"

"My uncle sent me here."

"Why did you jump on me . . ." Brown started to ask, but Mr. Minor interrupted quickly. "I'm sorry you are here with us, but that offer still goes. Our lawyer will get you out."

"Thank you," Ikomu said. "Although I arrived in this country recently, I do know of the cause for which you fight."

"You are African," Mr. Minor mused, "perhaps the cause of freedom and equality may not be so much yours as I thought. We have twenty million Negroes in the United States. We believe that they are not getting the

32

rights that our American Constitution guarantees to every citizen. We are trying to. . . ."

"Tell him plainly!" Brown interrupted. "We Negroes used to be slaves in this country. White men took off our chains a hundred years ago, but they never threw them away. They got 'em rusting in their minds and hearts. We want freedom and equality, but we won't get it unless we hold a gun to their heads."

"That's enough!" The minister was shouting, but Brown ignored him.

"Walkin' around with signs and sittin' in restaurants waitin' 'til doomsday to get served—where's it got us? See these scars, that's what it's got me! And they tell me, 'Be patient, move slowly, maybe your grandchildren will taste freedom.' To hell with my grandchildren! What about me—now? Gimme a bomb and I'll show you how to get things done."

"You're talking like a Black Muslim." Florence drew back in horror.

"So what!" Brown retorted sharply. "At least they know how things really stand. This is the third time in jail for me—picketin', sit-ins and demonstrations. I'm not thrilled about it like you. You think the whole world will change because you're sittin' in prison. I haven't seen anyone change except myself, and that's for the worse 'cause I don't believe in anything anymore."

"Truly a Bahutu," Ikomu said.

33

"What do you mean?"

"When I saw you in the picket line, I was not sure. With your American clothes, it was difficult to be certain. But your black skin, the shape of your head, your nose, your lips—all are those of a Bahutu. Negroes in America are not aware of these differences." The African's words were disdainful. "You think you are all the same. There are hundreds of tribes in Africa and an African knows to what tribe another belongs simply by observing his physical features. After hearing what you have just said about bombs, I *know* you are a Bahutu."

"I was born and raised in this country," the Bomber said defensively. "I don't know what's a Bahutu, but it's obvious you don't like them. Is that why you jumped me?"

"I am sorry about that," Ikomu apologized. "You cannot be blamed for having the characteristics of your ancestors. But the sight of you brought back unpleasant memories of Bahutus—and—well, sometimes when I am excited, I cannot control my actions."

"But why should you dislike Bahutus so?" asked Florence.

"Until only a year ago they were the slaves of my tribe. I am a Watusi and my father was king of the Watusis until—well, it no longer matters. Someone who thinks like *him*," he pointed to Brown, "gave the Bahutus some bombs. Now they are free."

34

Bomber Brown grinned with delight. His idea had been proved right in practice! "That's the only way to get your freedom," he crowed, "with bombs!"

"One of their bombs killed my father," Ikomu continued. "Those of my people who survived are in prison or enslaved. Some, like myself, escaped to another country. My uncle sent me to America to prepare myself to return and lead my people."

"Lead them to what?" Mr. Minor asked.

Ikomu hesitated. "I don't know. If I follow the suggestion of this Bahutu, I will return with bombs. But more people will be killed, and what is to prevent the Bahutus from doing the same again? I am a little confused. If Father Peurot were here, he could. . . ."

"Father Peurot?" Florence interrupted.

Ikomu lowered his eyes. "He was my teacher, but I —I was not a good pupil."

"There is a better way than bombs," the white man said, earnestly. "Join our movement. Learn what we do, and take it back to Africa. Demonstrations, sit-ins, passive resistance—these are the ways to achieve equality and freedom for all people on earth."

"Are you a Christian?" Ikomu asked.

"I am a minister in a Christian church."

"Is that like a priest?"

"Yes."

"But you do not talk like Father Peurot."

"I don't know how Father Peurot talked," the minister replied, "but I'm sure that as a Christian he wanted everyone to be equal and free."

"It was always his dream," Ikomu went on. "He lived and worked only for the day that Bahutu and Watusi would live together as brothers. With my father, he was preparing me to be ruler of such a kingdom—until the bombs. But Father Peurot never told me of the things of which you speak. Once I asked him, 'Father, if everyone in my kingdom should become free and equal, what will prevent some Bahutu peasant from sitting beside me on the throne and eating from my table? Where will we get enough food to give everyone an equal share?' Father Peurot answered, 'First you must have the orange in your hand. Then you may worry about how to divide it.' When he saw that I did not understand this saying, he added, 'There is no sense in talking about freedom and equality for everyone until you are free yourself. Strive first for your own freedom.' "

"I've heard that line before," Bomber Brown sneered. "If you're the son of a king, what do you know about equal rights? You probably had everything you wanted served up to you by some—Bahutu!"

"I once believed I was independent and even superior to those around me. I could go where I wished and do as I pleased, yet Father Peurot never considered me free. 'Someday perhaps you will be free,' he would say, 'but right now you are the worst kind of slave, for you do not even know who is your master.' I never understood him until the night. . . ."

Ikomu stopped as if someone had put a hand across his mouth. He stared at Brown and the fierce fire in the African's eyes rekindled. "Bahutu, treacherous Bahutu, murderous Bahutu, slave—enemy!" The words pounded in his mind, but other words also battered to be heard—an old priest's voice, that night in the jungle, and now this moment, right here. The struggle that went on within Ikomu was so violent that anyone watching him could see the battle lines drawn on his face. The smoke cleared; two small candles remained burning in his eyes, hot tears fell from them like melting wax.

Florence felt sorry for him, though she didn't know why. "Maybe you don't understand the situation in this country," she felt obliged to explain. "Some of our people are not able to go wherever they wish, as you say you could in Africa, because their skin is not white. We were picketing a restaurant and some of us were sitting inside, waiting to be served, because the owner won't let Negroes eat there. Sometimes we have to do the same at a school or a church because people have not overcome their prejudices."

She waited, wishing that Ikomu would say something, but he remained silent.

"I found that I couldn't even go with my Negro

37

friends. People would stare at us and if they didn't curse out loud, you could read their evil thoughts and sense their hatred as if they were pointing a death ray at us." Florence's voice rose and her expression changed to one of anger. "How can anyone think that way about others? People in this country have a right to go with anyone they please and wherever they please. Our constitution guarantees all Americans this freedom. Why should anyone be deprived of these rights because his skin is a different color? Why should . . . ?"

She stopped and groped for more to say. Ikomu's silence disturbed her. She never had difficulty finding words to explain her cause to a white person. It made sense to tell white people that they shouldn't be prejudiced against Negroes, but how do you talk to a Negro who considers other Negroes his enemies and slaves? The subject concerned freedom and equality, all right, but she had to find another handle to grip it by. Florence became aware that all her arguments in support of her activities had been given with a solid white audience in mind. Even when the words on her lips were: "*People* must be tolerant; *people* must love and accept; *people* must overcome their prejudices; *people* must be impartial to all"—these "people" all had *white* skins.

Now a *black* man with prejudices stood in their midst!

"What is that pin on your sweater?" Ikomu asked.

Florence bent her head to look at the white hand clasping the black. "This is a symbol of our group." She beamed. "We believe in the brotherhood of all races, but some people still can't accept others as brothers."

"Do you?" Ikomu asked.

"Why, yes—of course." Florence was surprised at the question. "At least I try to."

"Then why don't you wear a pin with two white hands clasping each other?" Ikomu asked. "It seems to me you have more need to make brothers of whites than of blacks."

"But the pin isn't meant for me!" Florence exclaimed. "It's to show others what we believe in, that black and white people should live together as friends and brothers. If everyone felt as I do, we wouldn't need such pins or any civil rights movement."

"And then all people would be free and equal and live as brothers?"

"Well, yes—I think so." Florence didn't seem sure. If the color barrier disappears, she thought, would other walls separate people? What kind of walls? Certainly they *couldn't* be as high?

Mr. Minor rescued Florence from her embarrassment. "In our country one barrier between men is based on race and we are trying to eliminate it. When we have succeeded in that, we shall start on other barriers."

39

"You do not talk like Father Peurot," Ikomu repeated.

"There he goes again," Brown exclaimed impatiently. "Who cares how your Father Peurot talks! Too many people talk too much anyway. Give me a bomb, and I'll show you what real talk sounds like. Your Father Peurot, whoever he is, is just like all the rest—a mouthful of empty words that couldn't chase a fly off his lip. I don't know him, but if he's anything like you. . . ."

WHAM!!!

Brown was on his back on the floor before he knew what hit him. Ikomu scrambled astride the startled man, pinning his arms under his knees. He grabbed the helpless Bomber by the neck and shook him so viciously his head banged against the floor.

"Bahutu—treacherous Bahutu!" the African shouted.

Mr. Minor tried vainly to pull them apart. Florence screamed for the guard, who ran into the room and helped the minister force Ikomu's hands apart. Puffing with exertion, the guard yanked Ikomu erect, twisted his arms behind his back and snapped handcuffs on his wrists.

Florence knelt beside the dazed Brown. "Get away from me with your damn love." He pushed her away and pointed a finger at Ikomu. "He's right! That's the way, black man! Beatings and blood! You got the taste of it! But it's only the beginning. Join me when we get out of here, black man. Put your strength together with mine and we'll make bombs—plenty of bombs. Boom—wheeee—boom!! One under every white man's house in the whole goddamn country. And I'll stand by the detonator. 'Give us freedom now!' I'll tell 'em, and I hope to God they say 'No!' so I can blast 'em all to hell!"

When Brown laughed, a hundred years of hatred broke out into an ugly roar.

"You'd better come out," the guard said to the two whites.

"You can't leave them alone together," the minister protested.

The guard led Ikomu out. "You can stay in there alone for a while until you cool off," he tossed at the Bomber. "I'll put this one in a cell for awhile."

Brown looked up. "I'll be waiting for you, black man," he shouted. "We'll get bombs!"

Ikomu stood alone in the center of a cell, arms hand-cuffed behind his back. He hadn't even heard Brown's invitation. His thoughts drifted backward again.

Three Bahutus appeared, men stripped naked, tied together by a rope wrapped tightly around their elbows and wrists. They were being urged along by Ikomu who held the loose end of the rope in one hand and a revolver in the other. Father Peurot half-trotted in an effort to keep up.

"You are making a mistake to take these men," the priest panted.

"They have killed my father and when we cross the border I shall kill them."

"But they weren't anywhere near the palace when the bomb exploded," Father Peurot protested. "You came across them in the fields while we were fleeing."

"They are Bahutus," Ikomu replied. "That is enough to make them guilty."

His teacher tried to appeal to his reason. "We still have a long way to go before we are safe across the border. Leave these men here; they are only delaying our escape."

Ikomu gave no answer but pulled sharply on the rope and cursed at the Bahutus. "Slaves you were and slaves you will remain! But this time I will tighten your chains until you fall dead at my feet!"

"And what about your own chains, Ikomu?"

"Once I am across the border with my uncle, I shall be safe and free to prepare for my return. Nothing shall prevent me from sitting on my father's throne."

"Yes, you will sit on the throne," the old priest sighed, "but that will not make you free. When will you stop being slave to your anger and to your desire for vengeance? Ever since you were a boy these tyrants have held you in their power. Their dominion will destroy you, along with your father's kingdom."

"Only Bahutus have destroyed," Ikomu answered. "But at least three of them will destroy no more." He jerked on the rope so hard that one of the naked men fell, pulling the other two down with him.

Father Peurot stopped pleading. Ikomu was in no condition to listen to reason. It was wiser now to concentrate on escaping from the madness that had swallowed up the jungle and turned both Bahutu and Watusi into wild beasts. Perhaps later Ikomu could be made to understand.

"Let's rest for a few hours," the old priest suggested. "We still have a full day's march remaining, and we'll need strength for it."

Much as Ikomu wanted to keep on, he saw that his exhausted teacher could not keep pace. Reluctantly, he tied the end of the rope to a tree and dropped to the ground. As soon as he did so, he realized that he himself had scarcely been off his feet since the Bahutu revolt began two days ago. It took very little urging to get the young prince to agree to let Father Peurot stand the first watch over the Bahutus and beasts of the night. Almost immediately Ikomu fell asleep; he might have slept the night through had not shouts awakened him.

The startled Watusi's eyes darted toward the tree—

the three Bahutus and Father Peurot were gone. Shouts came from the direction of the jungle road. Ikomu grabbed his revolver and ran through the brush until he saw the figures of the Bahutus in the moonlight ahead. Where was the priest? He fired into the air—he dared do nothing else lest he hit Father Peurot by mistake. The Bahutus scattered and disappeared down the road.

Father Peurot lay sprawled upon the ground. He had been savagely beaten; his white robes were stained with blood. Ikomu knelt beside him and gently eased his thigh under the injured man's head.

"I am sorry, Ikomu," the old priest said in a weak voice. "I wanted to lead them to the road and let them go back to their fields. Perhaps they misunderstood my intentions."

"Misunderstood! Oh, Father, don't you know the treachery of the Bahutus?" Ikomu glared up at the tree-tops and beyond; he clenched his fists. "God curse them for this, and all their children—curse them all!"

"Ikomu," Father Peurot said softly, "curses return to him who utters them. Leave them in peace."

The grief-stricken prince tried to wipe away some of the blood, but the more he wiped, the faster it flowed.

"Do not trouble yourself." Father Peurot placed his hand on Ikomu's arm. "You will finish your journey alone."

"No! I shall not leave this country until I find them and kill them for this."

"You have always fought the wrong battles," the old priest scolded. "Give me a final moment of peace. Promise me you will leave immediately. Do not try to return until you are free—until you have become the son of the king."

"But I *am* free; I *am* the son. . . ." Ikomu couldn't say another word. The old priest's smile shattered his protest. He raised his hand to bless Ikomu—it fell to his side.

"Hey, Ikomu!" The cell door rattled. "Ikomu, get up!"

Ikomu knelt on the floor, sitting back on his heels, his arms still held behind him by the handcuffs and his head lowered. He thought he saw blood on the floor, but the shouting washed it away. Raising his head, he saw the prison guard and Mr. Minor standing outside the cell.

"Our lawyer has arranged for your bail; you will be freed," Mr. Minor said.

"Come on, get up!" the guard said.

Ikomu stared at the men dully. It was obvious to the two observers that he was in a semi-trance.

The guard unlocked the cell and entered. He leaned over and unlocked the handcuffs.

45

"Come on, get up!" he repeated. "Don't you understand? You're free!"

Slowly, Ikomu started to rise; he wavered and almost fell. Mr. Minor sprang to his side, the guard close behind him. Together, they supported the shaking prince and half-carried him to the door of the cell.

As they crossed the sill, Ikomu's eyes began to clear. He shook off his supporters and cried, "I am the son of the king; I am. . . ."

He looked down the long, dim, jail corridor and asked the waiting men sadly:

"Are you able to make me free?"

2 Work Camp

"CHANGE INTO THIS BEFORE I TEAR THOSE RAGS OFF you," the cook shouted, and she began to do just that. She swung her right arm—it appeared to weigh as much as the man she berated—and ripped the sleeve off his shirt. The man backed timidly away.

By the time the work campers, eating dinner in the next room, reached the kitchen door to investigate, the cook had trapped the terrified man in a corner and was methodically tearing the shirt off his back. The cook was strong, and the shirt was badly worn; in moments the remains of the shirt fell to the floor. The man stood naked from the waist up; his ribs stuck out so that even from the other side of the kitchen they could easily be counted.

"Put this on," the cook snapped. She held the blue

flannel shirt as you might hold a coat for someone to slip into. The bony arms slid easily through the sleeves, and the woman buttoned the shirt and tucked in the tails. As she stepped back to appraise her handiwork, her hapless victim, face red and eyes lowered, scurried through the work campers, who moved to let him pass. Just before he reached the door, the man took something from his wrist and dropped it on the table. Then he hurried out.

The cook threw up her hands in disgust when she saw what he had left. She thought of running after him, but knew it would be futile. Though the miserable wretch might be no match for her strength—well, even a feeble antelope can outrun a hippopotamus.

"You idiot!" The cook shook her fist at the door. "Wait till you come back!"

"And why are you standing there like noodles?" she asked the work campers. "Was my cooking so bad that it couldn't keep you at the table until you'd finished?"

Though many of the campers were new to the schloss, they knew from the old-timer Latvian refugees that they could ill afford the enmity of the cook. She, like the Latvians, had survived fifteen years of postwar hardships at the settlement. Unlike the Latvians—engrossed in building new homes on the grounds of the schloss—the cook was already established. Her kitchen was her domain, and she ruled it absolutely!

"Did you see what happened?" she continued. "I told him it wasn't my shirt! I didn't buy it. No one here bought it. It came in one of those packages from America, and still he would not take it. Now he has left his watch as payment. A hundred shirts can be bought with this watch!"

A small figure passed by on the path outside the window. The cook flung the window up and bellowed, "Igon, you are an idiot! Wait till you come back!"

That night three of the work campers who had witnessed the incident in the kitchen retired to their room on the second floor of the stables. The room was quite livable, thanks to some of the refugees who were skilled carpenters and masons and to previous work campers who had come from many countries to work with them.

Had the first floor of the stables remained as it was when the schloss' former owner kept his prize stallions there, it too could have been converted into very comfortable living quarters. But the refugees had long since turned it into a shelter for the swine and their herdsman—none other than Igon, the victim of the cook's kindness.

"I'd like to know more about that guy," said Fred. Fred knew he would have to tell many stories about his summer in Europe when he returned to school in America. He wanted a good story to relate.

"Why waste your time?" asked Manfried, who came from East Germany. "He's an idiot, as the cook said."

"Did you ever hear of anyone giving his watch for a used shirt? There's something about him—worth finding out," Fred replied.

"Tomorrow, make inquiry," Barsam advised, and that's all he said. He pulled the covers over his head and went to sleep.

"Some roommate," Fred remarked. "During the day he won't speak two words because he's so busy working, and at night he just lies on his bed and listens. When he finally does say something, he goes to sleep so fast you can't even argue with him."

"If you want to talk that much," Manfried said, "then get up with him in the morning."

"At four-thirty? Are you kidding?"

Barsam and his people were accustomed to rising early. He could barely remember fleeing Palestine, but he would never forget the beauty of the sun's red lip touching the horizon over the hills of Jerusalem. Then, as in Jordan today, the women rose to prepare the fire and cook, the men to pray. Although he was only seventeen, Barsam liked to count himself among the men. He walked with them to pray in the fields and, on special occasions, to the stone Syrian Orthodox church. Barsam preferred the church because of the golden icon above the altar. It caught the first rays of the sun and tossed them back upon the churchgoers as if it were sending an answer to each prayer.

At the schloss, Barsam had no church to go to, no friends to walk with when he left the stables at dawn. He would wash with cold water from the pump and walk alone up the small hill behind the stables to greet the morning sun.

The two work campers had no difficulty getting the lowdown on Igon. Everyone at the schloss was more than willing to talk about him so long as someone would listen.

After dissecting, resurrecting, philosophizing and psychoanalyzing Igon's past, present and future, Fred and Manfried pieced together a story—how much was true, how much rumor, no one knew for sure.

Igon arrived at the schloss, clad only in the rags the boys had seen and carrying a half-full bag. He was delivered there by a group from another settlement, who claimed that he had come to them neatly dressed, bearing four pieces of luggage. No one knew what had happened in the meantime. It was rumored that he had been an officer in the Latvian army, forced to flee the country in such a hurry that he had left a wife and three small children behind—never to be heard from again. Though he appeared to be around sixty years old, he was actually only in his forties. He refused to speak or to eat and spent most of his time on a cot, in a near-stupor. If anything was forced upon him (as in the kitchen incident) he paid for it with something from his bag.

One day the cook ordered some of the men to bring Igon to the kitchen. She sat the man down, placed a bowl of thick soup before him and told him to eat. Igon just sat there.

"No one ever refuses to eat my food," the cook shouted. "Don't insult me!"

Igon tried to rise, but each time he attempted to get up the cook put her huge hands on his shoulders and pushed him down. Finally she grabbed the wooden mallet she used to flatten meat for schnitzels and waved it in front of Igon's face.

"I'm telling you for the last time—eat that soup or they'll have to carry you out." Her tone of voice and the look in her eyes startled Igon; he began to eat. The cook had not exaggerated the quality of her soup. Igon finished and held up the empty bowl in a mute plea for more.

That solved Igon's eating problem. When the dinner bell rang, he headed straight for the kitchen, and whatever the cook placed on his plate, he ate.

Slowly Igon regained his strength. One day the director suggested he help with the repair work. Igon was asked to lay bricks for a wall. In the evening when they came to find him, he was standing where they had left him—in one hand a brick, in the other the trowel. Not one brick had been laid, and the mortar in the bucket was hard as rock.

He was switched to setting windowpanes, but he broke one and lapsed again into depression. For two days he refused to eat, claiming he did not deserve food after such a blunder, but the cook and her wooden mallet straightened that out.

"Let him wash floors," someone suggested. "A child can do that and what could go wrong?" Igon washed the floor; he seemed content, though you couldn't tell because he never smiled. Someone walked across the newly washed floor, a board squeaked, and Igon moaned, "I've spoiled it by too much water!" The director tried, in vain, to convince him that the floor had squeaked for at least a hundred years; Igon fell into another fit of despair.

Igon was left alone until the woman who fed the swine became ill. When it appeared she would not recover for several weeks, the director looked for someone to replace her. "Use Igon," one man suggested. "No, don't! The swine will starve to death!" But Igon it was, for there was no one else available.

They gave him simple instructions—pick up the garbage and dump it into the troughs. Early in the morning he carried the garbage from the kitchen to the door of the stables. He staggered under the weight of the heavy barrel; it slipped to the ground, and Igon with it. Minutes passed and still he sat in his familiar stupor. The swine were hungry for their morning garbage and began to protest. The whole herd joined in a screeching chorus. Igon roused from his trance as though a hypnotist had snapped his fingers. He opened the stable door hurriedly, dumped the garbage into the troughs, and watched the swine plunge their snouts into it.

Some of the refugees said that the squeals from the swine made Igon realize for the first time that living creatures were depending on him to stay alive. Others thought it was simply the shock caused by the sudden and unusual noise. Whatever the explanation, one point was clear—once Igon became their herdsman, the swine had never had it so good! He mixed the garbage with water and cereals to make it tastier; he cleaned the pens each day and laid in fresh straw; he washed the swine if they returned too muddy from the fields; he even went to the woods and, with his bare hands, picked the stinging nettle plants that swine especially like to eat.

One night Fred and Manfried were discussing Igon, as usual. This time Barsam sat on the edge of his bed and listened. He even contributed what he had heard from others and seen for himself. Since he began feeding the swine, Igon was doing the work of ten men. He was sweeping walks, feeding the geese, laying bricks (he soon became the fastest bricklayer), gardening, washing, cleaning, chopping firewood, accepting any task given to him. From dawn until too dark to see, Igon worked. He stopped only when the dinner bell rang. Then he walked to the kitchen, sat at the table and waited for the cook to put a plate of food before him. Through the whole day he spoke hardly a word, and he never smiled. That seemed to disturb the refugees even more than had his former moods of depression. If anything is needed in a refugee camp, it's a smile.

"It's obvious to me," said Manfried, "that the man is mentally ill. I think he should be put away. Something might give him a shock and make him violent."

"He's as gentle as a lamb," Barsam declared flatly.

"Everytime I see him, I say 'hello' but he never answers," Fred argued.

"Maybe he doesn't understand English."

"I thought of that. But I tried 'guten Tag' and 'bonjour' and got no response. I even asked some of the refugees how to say it in Russian and Latvian, but they told me not to bother, because Igon doesn't answer anyone's greeting."

"Manic-depressive," Manfried judged. "Watch out for him."

Fred wasn't convinced that they should avoid Igon. The purpose of a work camp was not just to build things of brick and stone, it was to help restore the morale and spiritual ideals of the refugees. And who needed such restoration more than Igon? "There may be good grounds for his behavior," Fred reasoned. "How do we know what he has suffered?"

"I'll tell you exactly," replied Manfried. "He used to be an officer in the Latvian army and was very wealthy. When war came he fled, no doubt with all the money and jewelry he could carry. I know his kind of refugee. All his life he amassed fortunes through the misery of others. I can assure you that his flight has brought untold happiness to a thousand peasants in Latvia who have his land, and that's exactly how it should be. I have little sympathy for the man."

"How do you know this?" Barsam demanded.

"I've got a nose for ex-aristocrats," Manfried answered, smiling. "They have a particular smell. Well—maybe I am exaggerating. But you're from Jordan and Fred's from America, so what do you know about refugees? I've known hundreds who fled from East Germany and I can tell you—good riddance!"

"How about yourself?" Fred said.

"I am *not* a refugee. I am a student with a legal exit permit and when I have finished my studies, I shall return to East Germany and work for my Fatherland."

"You mean for the Communists," Fred said.

Manfried snapped back: "You Americans are all

alike! If someone doesn't think as you do, you call him Communist! I am a Christian—that is why I am in this work camp. But if I had known I would have to live in the same room with an American, just one floor above an idiot, I'd never have come."

"If you're really a Christian," argued Fred, "you would welcome the opportunity to help an unfortunate creature like Igon."

"And how would you go about that?" Manfried asked, smiling again.

"I don't know, but at least I wouldn't judge him or avoid him. Maybe we could convince the director that he ought to be put in a hospital where he could get special treatment. Lots of cases of mental illness come from a physical ailment. An operation might help."

"There's nothing wrong with his body," Manfried scoffed.

"How do we know? And if there isn't, we could send him to a psychiatrist or a hypnotist."

"A what?"

"A hypnotist. Someone who can put you to sleep and make you forget past experiences. In America, hypnotists have helped many people break habits like smoking and drinking. If some unpleasant memories are causing Igon's depression, a hypnotist could help him."

"About the only thing that could help him would be

a heart attack," Manfried said. "Let death end his suffering. He's a miserable wretch the way he is and a burden on everyone else."

Barsam sprang from the cot and unleashed a tirade as surprising for its length as for its loudness. "He is no burden to anyone! He does more work in the morning before you get out of bed than both of you do together in a whole day. And he doesn't eat a tenth of what you stuff into your bellies. Some burden! He won't even let the laundry woman wash his clothes. And who do you think cleans up around the pump after you leave your dirt there?"

Manfried's face reddened; Fred gloated until Barsam turned the attack on him:

"And what a Good Samaritan you are! You want to send him to a hospital, send him to a psychiatrist, send him to a hypnotist, send him anywhere so the sight of him won't bother you, and you can dream that he is being helped. One of my countrymen had a sick brother. The doctors could not help him; they just said he was incurable and that he would die. My friend put his brother on his back and carried him twenty miles to the waters of the Jordan River. He washed his brother's diseased body in the river and carried him to pray at the church on the banks of the river. In the church was an icon of the Virgin Mary." Barsam paused for breath.

"Don't tell me, let me guess," Fred jibed. "A miracle happened and the sick man was healed."

"Yes," Barsam replied, "but I do not like the way you speak of this as if it were a joke."

"Look, Barsam, if sick people in your country seek to be cured like this, it's understandable. After all, you haven't any doctors or hospitals or medicines which we have in more civi — in America or Europe, I mean. But what has that to do with us and with Igon?"

"You don't expect us to believe that your friend was miraculously cured?" Manfried was incredulous.

"Why not?"

"Haven't you heard? This is the twentieth century! We no longer believe in fairy tales."

"Or in God," Barsam interjected sadly.

"What has belief in God got to do with this?" Manfried asked. "If your friend was really healed, then there's a perfectly sound scientific explanation for it. But don't drag in this miracle stuff as if God himself came down and healed him."

Barsam was sad; he didn't want to talk anymore. He walked back to his cot and began to undress. One man says there is a God, he thought, and another says there is none; what is the difference when neither believes that God can do anything on earth?

Barsam went to bed. Fred and Manfried skipped

61

their usual tête-à-tête and did likewise without another word. A half hour passed, and though no one spoke each knew that the others were awake. They could hear an occasional grunt from a swine in the stables below. Fred lifted his head from the pillow and whispered, "Barsam."

Barsam turned toward the voice.

Fred pointed a finger toward the floor. "How would *you* help the guy down there?"

"I would carry him for twenty miles," Barsam replied, "but there is no icon here."

Thoughts about Igon continued to trouble the three roommates. They heard the younger refugees call him "idiot," laugh at him and tease him. They saw the older ones shake their heads in sorrow. Igon's sad face seemed to leave a scar on everyone's heart. "If only he would smile," they said among themselves. "We too have had our troubles in this war—who hasn't?—but that is over now. What will happen to us and to our children, if we cannot put aside the darkness that has filled our lives?"

Sometimes it seemed that Igon had no time to smile. Certainly the jobs that kept him busy most of the day were nothing to create cheerfulness. He never lingered to listen to the humorous stories the refugees delighted in sharing. In order to change Igon's mood, one would first have to manage to be with him long enough.

"I thought I had a chance today," Fred told his roommates one night. "I was on the detail carrying bricks and mortar for Igon. I did everything to be friendly. I smiled, I joked with him, I told him he was the fastest bricklayer I ever saw, I asked him questions about his past, I talked about my family in America, I told him why we came to the schloss, I asked him how the pigs were getting along, I invited him to come to our worship services, I told him. . . ."

"If you did so much talking," Barsam interrupted, "who carried the bricks and mortar?"

Fred blushed. "I admit we didn't get much of the wall finished. The only words he said to me during the whole day were 'more bricks.' When it was time to quit, I was so tired and depressed I couldn't eat."

"Why waste energy?" Manfried remarked. "When I had that duty, do you think I let him rush me? Two bricks at a time, that's all I carried. And I didn't break speed records supplying them to him. When he got ahead of me, he had to wait and I let him know by the expression on my face that he wasn't going to make me move any faster. Anyone who's mentally deficient has the strength of a gorilla, so let him work like one. As for me, I'll get by with my brains."

63

"With those brains you couldn't get downstairs into the pigpen," Fred said.

And that started another loud exchange of opinion that in turn sent Barsam to his usual place of refuge under the blanket. He would have liked to talk about Igon, but each time the conversation started off with Igon, it changed quickly, and then changed again. Inevitably, it concluded with Fred calling Manfried a Communist and Manfried retorting, "You Americans are all alike. . . ."

One morning Barsam went for his morning ablutions as usual; Igon was already there, working the pump with one hand and washing with the other. Barsam did not pause for a greeting; he took the handle and began pumping. The startled Igon stopped both pumping and washing but the water, now swiftly pouring out, splashed all over him. He plunged both hands under the pump, washed quickly, turned on his heel and headed back to the stables as if no one else was present.

Barsam continued to operate the pump with one hand; cupping his free hand, he caught the cold water and splashed it on his face. The pump handle began to move faster; it was Igon returning the favor.

From that time on, each sunrise while everyone else at the schloss slept, the two met to pump water for each other; never a word passed between them. When they finished, Barsam walked up the hill alone, and Igon departed in the opposite direction to pick up the garbage from the kitchen.

The rising sun was like a second bath for Barsam. Its golden rays made him feel purified inside. Each morning he stood on the hill for a long time until the thoughts that stirred in him stopped their chatter. The silence cleansed his mind and heart—nothing existed for him except the glories of God, which he could find neither words to describe nor praises to sing. After the silence settled in him, Barsam would descend from the hill; his only regret was that he could not lay the fullness of his heart before the icon in the stone church of his village.

Often he could see Igon on the path below carrying garbage to the swine, and his heart went out to this poor "idiot." Though the boy had fled from Palestine, and the man from Latvia, both knew a common anguish —that of the refugee. Like a shrub torn from the bed that had nourished it and planted in rocky soil, the refugee needed time to regain full strength and beauty. During several seasons the shrub might suffer, part might even die, and that part would have to be cut away. Pity the poor bush that landed in the garden of an impatient man who could not, or would not, understand why it drooped.

Each time Barsam saw the Latvian, he cried to himself, "*I* would be glad to carry him twenty miles to the icon—oh, for a miracle!" One morning as he descended from the hill, an object in the direction of the stables caught the sun's rays and reflected them into Barsam's eyes. "Can it be?" he asked, and left the path to cut across the field. Halfway across he cried out, "It *is* the golden icon!" And he began to run. When he reached the stable door over which the shining object hung, Barsam realized he had been deceived. It was not a miraculous icon, but a golden horseshoe which someone had nailed above the door, no doubt to bring good luck.

He stood there, trembling from the excitement. He didn't know whether to laugh at his foolishness or to weep over his disappointment, but he had no chance to do either because a voice behind him said:

"I painted it last night. It was covered with dirt."

The words appeared to come from a barrel of garbage.

"It is not real gold—just gilt paint," Igon added, straightening his back under his load.

Barsam stepped ahead and opened the door.

"Show me how to feed the swine," said the boy.

"Why?" asked Igon, as he unshouldered the barrel.

Barsam didn't know what to say; he didn't even realize he had asked the question. Why should he want to learn how to feed swine? In his country no one kept swine because few would eat the meat. Until he came to the schloss he had never even seen such an animal.

"Perhaps I can help feed them," Barsam replied.

Four enormous sows and a dozen pigs squealed wildly and threw themselves against the fence; they knew it was feeding time. First Igon cleaned and pitchforked fresh straw into the pens. Then he scraped out the troughs with his hand and mixed the food. He added potatoes and meal to fatten the pigs; for the sows—orange peels, greens, vegetables and potatoes were all stirred into a greenish liquid taken from a barrel standing in the corner.

Barsam watched the careful manner in which Igon prepared the food. From time to time he glanced at the swineherd's face—what a change of expression! The sadness had disappeared. Igon was wide awake; he smiled and explained. Barsam had never heard him talk so much.

"This one . . ." Igon said, pointing to a sow whose legs were bent under her own weight, "is very fussy—eats only cooked potatoes, not raw. One more week and her time will be up."

The herdsman poured the liquid, with some garbage and meal, into the troughs and stuck his arm in up to the elbow to swish the mixture around. When the food was ready, he unlatched the fences, and the pigs, squealing and shrieking, rushed out.

The fussy sow slurped once and hobbled back to the

corner of her stall. "Only lazy," laughed Igon. "I will give her a delicacy." He reached into a barrel and pulled out some green plants.

Barsam called out, "Let me feed her!"

"No, no!" said Igon, "this is not for you."

But before Igon could prevent him, Barsam thrust his hand into the barrel.

"Y-eeyoww!!" he screamed. "There's a bee in there!"

Igon doubled over with laughter. When he recovered, he grabbed Barsam's hand and shoved it into the greenish liquid in which the plants floated. "Those are stinging nettles," he grinned, "but this will soothe the pain."

The first sign of change that the other people living at the schloss noticed in Igon was the way he held his head. Instead of letting it hang low, he cocked it like a deer sensing someone's approach. His eyes were kind. Now when the younger refugees looked into them, they no longer said, or even thought, "idiot." The older Latvians stopped shaking their heads over him. They called to him, "Good morning, Igon," or "How are you today, Igon?" in joyous tones.

Because Igon's face brightened whenever Barsam came into sight all knew that the youth had something to do with this change. Had people of the schloss awakened at sunrise, they could have watched the two pump water for each other, feed the swine and sweep the walks. During the day, whenever an unpleasant task had to be accomplished (cleaning out the cesspool or spreading manure on the fields) they could always find Igon leading the work detail, Barsam at his side. The two tackled each job as cheerfully as children who do not yet realize that work is not fun—not something to avoid or to do grudgingly.

Fred and Manfried noticed the change, too. The American kept asking Barsam how he had managed to become friendly with Igon. Barsam replied that if the American really wanted to learn the "secret" all he had to do was rise at four-thirty the next morning and go downstairs to the stables. Fred agreed immediately, but that night he and Manfried engaged in another of their endless discussions. When Barsam shook him the next morning, Fred mumbled sleepily, "Stables? Who said anything about going to the stables at this hour? It's not even daylight." He turned and pulled the blanket over his head.

Manfried found nothing significant in the change. "Three more days and we return home—you to Jordan, Fred to America, and I to Germany," he said to Barsam, "but Igon stays here. You know what will happen! He will be lonelier than before and he will return to his idiot ways—only even worse."

"He gave me a jar of honey for my journey home," Barsam replied, "but I do not know what to leave him."

"Leave him—period! And after you have left, forget him," Manfried advised.

69

"I have thought of something I would like to do but it is difficult for me to do alone." Barsam hesitated.

Fred offered his assistance. Barsam explained that there was a Latvian church many miles from the schloss, an Orthodox church very like the one in his village in Jordan. The director was willing to provide a car.

"I suggested to Igon that we visit the church together this Sunday," Barsam continued. "At first he would not even consider it but I could see that the thought really appealed to him. I urged him even more and pointed out that this would be my last day at the schloss. Finally he admitted that even though he would like to go, it was out of the question. In the first place he had no proper clothes to wear and second. . . ."

"He can have my white shirt and suit," Fred interrupted. "He's about my size."

"That is already taken care of. The director has given him some clothes. But the other matter—Igon believes he cannot leave because there would be no one to feed the swine. I do not want to ask the other refugees to do this, especially on a Sunday, so I thought of my roommates. Igon and I would have to leave early in the morning because the church is far away. So you would have to feed the swine once in the morning and again in the evening."

"What time in the morning?" asked Fred.

Barsam smiled. "On Sundays the swine sleep late. You may feed them whenever you get up."

"OK," said Fred, and Manfried had little choice but to accept the proposition.

On Sunday morning the birds lined the branches like an honor guard and broke into song as Igon and Barsam passed beneath them on the path from the stables to the main house. The director was waiting with his car. Igon had never left the schloss before; it was rumored that he would be wearing a white shirt and a tie and suit. The people of the schloss were out in full force, most of them gathered on the lawn outside the house. One would think they were waiting for the arrival of some government dignitary.

"That is not Igon," someone in the crowd whispered, as the two approached.

"Certainly it is he," another replied. "Last night I myself cut his hair and shaved him. Look at the result! I am no ordinary barber, I am an artist!"

Barsam waved to the crowd. Igon nodded and smiled. The crowd applauded in unison, as if some unseen director had given them a cue. A little girl ran to Igon and handed him a white flower. As he bent down, she kissed him on the cheek. An old woman, standing by the car door, pressed a coin into Igon's hand and asked him to light a candle for her son in Latvia.

"And one for my wife," someone else shouted.

"For all of us," Igon said, as he climbed into the back seat beside Barsam. The crowd began to sing; the director waited until the song ended, then eased the car down the driveway.

Fred opened the stable door, sniffed, then closed it quickly without entering. "And to think I ate bacon this morning!" he said.

"Some people won't eat pork," Manfried said. "It's against their religion. But it has nothing really to do with religion. They don't have refrigeration to prevent the meat from spoiling, that's all it is."

"It's more than that," Fred disagreed. "They could kill the pig and eat him the same day; they do that with sheep and goats. There's something about a pig that prohibits them from eating its meat. I read somewhere that some of them would rather starve than eat the flesh of a pig."

"That's foolishness. It's hard enough as it is for this earth to provide food for all its inhabitants, so why should we pass up any opportunity? I think we ought to grind up the pork, put it in a can with a different label, and ship some to them. They won't know it's pork, and once they taste it, no pig will be safe among them."

"I know someone who was poisoned by eating canned pork. . . ."

The two work campers talked on and on. Indignant squeals issued from the stables, but the troughs remained empty—the herdsmen were busy deciding how to feed the world!

3 Flower

"GARDEN OF EDEN" WAS WHAT THE MEN FROM THE nearby airbase called the Bonnells' backyard. The housing development, in which Lieutenant Irving Bonnell lived, was run-of-the-mill; the wonderland his wife had created, right outside their kitchen door, was close to paradise.

Irving had met and married Hanako during his service in Tokyo. Everyone who strolled through her garden agreed that the English translation of Hanako—Flower—suited the Japanese bride admirably. Flower accepted her new name happily—it sounded more American—and from the day of her marriage she had done all she could to adjust to the new ways of her husband and his countrymen. She had sacrificed religion, country, culture, and most difficult of all—family.

Fortunately Flower didn't have to give up her green thumb. Her magic touch gave the plants in her garden a certain character of their own. They didn't wait to be looked at. They peeked out and flirted with you; they wrapped their fragrance around you like a lasso and pulled you to them; their brilliant colors coaxed your eyes into dancing. Even the rocks, bushes and dwarf trees, without a single bloom, were artfully arranged. The breezes sighed gently through the leaves of the shrubbery and the beautiful shapes of the rocks soothed you. A tiny brook that wound through the development washed the feet of all the plants and sang them to sleep in the evening.

It was no coincidence that so many people happened to drop by at the Bonnells. At first they came out of curiosity—to see the Japanese bride—later they came to admire the artistry of her hands. A friend at the airbase once confided to Irving, "When I'm all wound up after a fight with my wife or a rough day at the base, a walk through your garden relaxes me better than a shot of whiskey."

The garden was Flower's own special refuge. She had been born with a love for flowers. Her Tokyo neighbors believed that the gods had endowed her with a special gift and claimed that the lilies in Japan never stopped crying from the day she left. Flower had a reason of her own for planting her American garden. This only reminder of the past strengthened her to bear a burden that was becoming intolerable. The time she spent in the garden helped her store up energy for her daily encounters with her husband's mother.

Flower might not have survived her lonely struggle had not the gods intervened and sent her help in the form of her sister, Miyuko. Was it the gods? Or should we call it "chance"? It doesn't matter. For Flower and Miyuko it was the gods who brought them together again—the gods and the death of their father.

"It was Father's last wish that I come to America and stay with you a short while," Miyuko said, as the sisters sat alone in the garden. "He asked that I carry his blessings to you."

"Would that he had come himself," Flower replied, "that I might sit by his side and place a flower in his hand and tell him of my sorrow." She looked at her sister, and tears welled in the eyes of both. "I cannot stay here any longer. I shall ask my husband for a divorce and return with you to Japan."

"Perhaps it is as well that Father is not here," her sister admonished. "He would grieve over your words."

"I cannot help it, Miyuko. Do you think I have not tried to carry this burden? Two years ago my husband asked me if his mother could live with us. I urged him to arrange this. Why shouldn't she live with us? Her husband was dead. She was alone. It was our duty to care for her. I wanted to have her as my own mother, to love her as my own blood; I am no longer Hanako, I am Flower Bonnell, and I belong to my husband and to his family."

"Then why do you talk of divorce?"

"Because if I stay I shall die. Try to understand, Miyuko. Do you remember what happened to my flowers in Tokyo, whenever Shingawa visited us? He hated flowers. He never could enjoy them because he was old and almost blind. When he sat in our garden, waiting to collect the rent, the flowers around him drooped and lost their splendor. How much tender care I had to give them to bring life back to their petals, after he left. It is like that now. My husband's mother hates me, and I am slowly wilting in her shadow."

"And your husband?"

"Perhaps he does not know what is happening to me, for I have kept all this to myself. But he is aware that his mother does not like me. He thinks it will pass after we know each other better. Father was right when he told me I would face hardships in America. I am not afraid of them. Have I not learned from our father's own example how to face them? But here I do not recognize my enemy. Can you understand, Miyuko? Mrs. Bonnell is not my enemy. How can an unhealthy plant be my enemy? If a plant gets sick, I look for insects or weeds or disease. These are my enemies, and when I find them, I destroy them. But I do not know what ails my husband's mother; I have searched, but I cannot find it. I thought she was disturbed because my husband is her only child, or because I am a foreigner. But when we attend the Christian chapel at the airbase, she does not appear to be offended that the chaplain calls us all children of God, and sometimes after chapel she is very nice to me. I also thought perhaps she was jealous of my garden. But I have watched her walk alone among my flowers and caress them with her smile.

"You have not seen her yet, Miyuko. She has been to the city. When you meet her at dinner tonight you will understand why I must leave. She has planted a hedge of thorns between herself and me, and I do not know what feeds its roots. This is what torments me. How can I struggle against an unknown enemy?"

Miyuko rose from the bench and suggested that they walk a little. She chose the path along the brook, and as they proceeded she turned to her sister and said:

"When father warned you about hardships in America he also said, 'Everything can be overcome with love, even Shingawa's hatred of your flowers.' "

Flower smiled. She remembered the vase in her father's room. Each day she arranged fresh flowers in it; each day she threw out those from the day before. One day her father suggested that instead of throwing them out she should take the day-old flowers to Shingawa.

"Remember, though," her father cautioned, "the old man is nearly blind; you must describe the flowers to him."

"But how?"

In the most poetic language—it sounded as though her father spent all his time composing words to suit the flowers—he proceeded to tell her exactly what to say to the old landlord. She remembered one such poem well:

> The redness of this petal,
> like fire from a dragon's mouth,
> fills its admirer with wonder
> but burns its foe.

> As the gods have given beauty to the flowers
> that they may be above human frailties,
> so they arm that man with love
> whom they wish to protect from destruction.

Shingawa was delighted. He displayed the flowers for every passerby to see, and if anyone tarried, the old man repeated the poetic descriptions word for word. Clearly the words made him see each petal; they expressed his own delight.

"Shingawa was blind; only our words made his attitude change," Flower mused.

"But it was Father's love that brought out these

words," her sister replied. "Do you not believe that your love can direct you to Mrs. Bonnell's heart?"

Flower shrugged. "I am afraid my love is not as strong as Father's."

Miyuko's eye stopped at a small bed isolated by a circle of rocks. The flowers in it were stunted, the faded blossoms shriveled.

"What happened to this bed?" she asked.

"That belongs to my mother-in-law; she does not let me care for it. Some say she does this to spoil my garden, but that is not true. It is the hatred in her that causes everything she touches to wither and die. I *must* go away from her." Flower's voice was sad. "You cannot read the message of my flowers as I can. They are a mirror that reflects my inner life. I am aware of the slightest change in color, the smallest blemish on a leaf. If a worm brushes against a root, I see the pain written in the blossom. My flowers are losing their splendor, just as they did in the presence of Shingawa. The seeds of hatred must be sprouting in me also."

After a moment Flower lifted her head, smiled at her sister, and said, "But enough of me. Tell me of Father's last days. I know only what you have written."

"Our father's face was peaceful as the sunbeams fell upon it for the last time. Our mountain lakes were never so calm. He spoke of you. I think he knew from your letters that you were suffering, though you never wrote directly about it. He made me promise to come to you to bring his final blessing and to encourage you to remain loyal to the gods.

"Yes, he knew you became a Christian after your marriage. He asked me to read to him from Christian books so he, too, could learn of your new religion. The more I read, the more he wanted to hear. I was rereading a story from the Christian Bible, when Father interrupted me, 'It is all true, my child. If I were young and did not know the gods as I know them now, I would give up the religion of my ancestors and become a Christian. But for me it is not necessary. The gods have revealed to me the mystery of love and given me the strength to forgive and to ask for forgiveness. When you see your sister, tell her that her father has walked the path that lies before her as a Christian and he will be waiting for her at the end.' "

Miyuko paused to take a flower out of her handbag. Though it was pressed and dried, the flower was not withered like the blossoms in Mrs. Bonnell's flower bed. Its colors, though faded, still showed sparks of life. The younger girl carefully handed the flower to her sister and continued:

"This was the last flower you put into Father's vase. He would not let it be taken to Shingawa. I did not know he had kept it until the night he died. 'Return this flower to your sister as a sign of my blessing,' he said.

'May she use it to bring happiness to her household and peace to my soul.' "

Irving Bonnell's mother was not a witch. Miyuko realized this when she met Mrs. Bonnell shortly before dinner. The darkness in the older woman's eyes reminded the young Japanese girl of her father. There was one difference—the muscles in Mrs. Bonnell's face were tense; deep lines were etched from the bridge of her nose upward; the darkness was imprisoned in her eyes. The unlined face of Miyuko's father showed that he had made peace with his darkness.

"She suffers very much," Miyuko told her sister.

Flower nodded. "It is true but I cannot find out why."

At the dinner table the lieutenant was in a light mood. "How do you like the American we've made of your sister? Sometimes I think I prefer her the way she was in Tokyo."

"How was that, Irving?" his mother asked.

"She used to hit me the way the sunrise hits Mount Fuji and makes everything happy. I never could wait to get off duty to visit her. If you think her garden here is something, you should have seen the one she had in Tokyo! I almost wanted to apologize to the flowers for taking her away from them."

"If you liked it so much, why didn't you stay?" Mrs. Bonnell's tone was barbed.

"Oh, come on, Mother, I'm only kidding."

"May we go into the living room for tea?" Flower suggested. "My sister has brought me a tea set you may like to see."

"Let Miyuko serve it the way she did in Tokyo," her husband added. "When you see this, Mother, you'll want her to give lessons to your woman's club."

Flower went into the kitchen and the others walked to the living room. Mrs. Bonnell took a place on the sofa next to Miyuko and made small talk.

"Weren't you afraid to travel such a distance alone?"

"The stewardess on the plane was very kind. I felt at ease."

"Do Japanese girls still marry Americans in Japan?"

The unexpected question puzzled Miyuko. Her "Yes" was guarded.

"I understand many Japanese brides have left their American husbands and returned to Japan."

"I know of only one or two," Miyuko answered.

"Why do you think they return?"

"I do not know. They must be unhappy here."

"But I thought Japanese wives were specialists in love—and loyalty."

"They must have been very unhappy here."

"Do you think your sister is unhappy in America?"

"Cut it out, Mother!" snapped Irving. "What kind of question is that?"

FLOWER

Flower entered the room, bearing a small brazier filled with burning charcoal. This she placed on a mat in the center of the floor. She bowed deeply to her sister, who stood up, returned the bow and walked directly to the kitchen. Flower took Miyuko's place on the sofa next to Mrs. Bonnell. "If you do not mind," she said, "my sister will perform the duties of hostess for the tea ceremony. In Japan this is a special art, and not everyone is skilled at it. Miyuko is one of the best."

Miyuko reentered the room carrying a pair of metal tongs. She walked gracefully, without haste, and placed the tongs beside the brazier. She returned to the kitchen twice more, and each time she placed the utensils carefully, exactly where each item belonged. After the third trip, she knelt on the floor before the brazier and sat back on her heels. Her body was erect yet relaxed.

Miyuko lifted the tongs and pecked at the charcoal. So carefully did she move the unburnt pieces from the edge to the center that she appeared to be creating an artistic design out of the smoldering lumps. Precisely she returned the tongs to their proper place.

Without a quiver her hands lifted the iron kettle slowly onto the grill.

Flower and the lieutenant maintained the appropriate silence until the water bubbled into a boil. Mrs. Bonnell made no attempt to speak either. She appeared entranced by the graceful flowing movements of the Japa-

85

nese girl—the way Miyuko dipped a bamboo spoon into the bowl of powdered green tea and transferred three spoonfuls (no one larger or smaller than the other) into the empty tea cup before her. Then she sank the long bamboo dipper deep into the kettle and drew it out overflowing with hot water. She held the dipper over the kettle for a moment, poured exactly one-third of the water over the tea powder in the cups and returned the rest to the kettle. She picked up the bamboo whisk that looked like a shaving brush, gripped it firmly yet without tension, and beat the mixture in the tea bowl as one would whip cream—until it was frothy. There was never the slightest haste. Miyuko's complete attention was focused on each movement. Her thoughts did not wander to the previous maneuver or to the one ahead. Mrs. Bonnell had the feeling that had she interrupted the girl at any point in the ceremony, she could have returned a week later and continued from the exact place she left off.

During the fifteen minutes of the tea ceremony the three watchers experienced a strange feeling. They were no longer aware of each other's presence. Tea was being prepared—they knew that; but Miyuko, the person preparing it, had disappeared. They heard only the "wind in the pines"—the bubbling water in the kettle—and they saw only the perfect harmony of movements leading to one goal—the preparation of a cup of green tea.

All three awaited that tea with unrestrained anticipation.

Miyuko cupped the tea bowl in both hands, bowed and placed it before the lieutenant. He put the bowl on the palm of his left hand and, supporting the side of the bowl with his right hand, he sipped.

"Ah, Miyuko," Irving said with a smile, "not even in your beautiful Japan could the flavor of your tea excel this." She bowed, and he handed the bowl to his mother.

Mrs. Bonnell sipped from the bowl twice and complimented Miyuko: "I have never enjoyed waiting for my cup of tea as I have today." She continued to hold the bowl.

Her son whispered to her, "Mother, you're supposed to pass the bowl to Flower."

She turned and offered the bowl to her daughter-in-law. For a brief moment their eyes met. Flower was stunned. Is this the face of my husband's mother? The same darkness shadowed the older woman's eyes, but the tense lines in her face had disappeared. The turmoil had been replaced by tranquility. How like Father she looks, Flower thought.

Flower complimented her sister and drank the rest of the tea in the bowl. Then she helped her sister carry away the utensils. When they reached the kitchen, Flower asked, "Did you see her face? I have never seen such an expression before. It almost reminded me of Father."

"I noticed it when I first met her," Miyuko answered. "You have been away from Father too long—perhaps you do not remember."

"No, I could never have missed this before. Something happened to her during the tea ceremony—something that removed the hedge of thorns. Did you see? The tenseness in her face was gone! If only I could discover the hedge! I'd tear it up by its roots and burn it in the fire. If it were gone forever, Miyuko, I would have a mother again!"

"And your father," added her sister.

"But the hedge will grow back and the thorns will be sharper."

Flower was right. The hedge had grown back by the time the sisters returned to the living room; the lines furrowed more deeply than ever in Mrs. Bonnell's face. Her words pricked them sharply. "It's really not necessary to hide in the kitchen to talk behind our backs. You can speak in Japanese right before us, and we won't know what you really think of us."

The two sisters exchanged glances and did not speak. Flower took her place on the sofa, Miyuko on a stool.

"The tea was charming," Mrs. Bonnell said to Miyuko, but her insincerity made the girl understand her sister's comparison to a thorny hedge. She flinched as the older woman went on, "You must teach me the ceremony before you return to Japan. When do you expect to go back?"

"I have not thought about it," Miyuko replied. "Perhaps in a few weeks."

"You're welcome here as long as you wish to stay," her brother-in-law offered. "I won't be surprised if you never go back. When the bachelors at the base get a look at you, they'll fall like a ton of bricks."

"I do not understand what you mean," Miyuko said.

Flower tried to explain the expression to her in Japanese, but Mrs. Bonnell interrupted angrily, "Stop it! I don't want to hear that language in this house!"

"Mother, for God's sake, she's only trying to explain what I said!"

"I don't care. I don't want sneaky talk in my presence!"

There was a complete silence until Mrs. Bonnell, with an obvious effort, regained control of herself. This time she spoke slowly and distinctly to Miyuko, "What my son means is that you have come here to get an American husband."

"I didn't say that!"

Mrs. Bonnell ignored her son's protest. "Isn't that the goal of every Japanese girl? They couldn't conquer us with their sneaky bombs but they're succeeding with their geisha girls!"

"It would be an honor to marry an American as kind as your son," Miyuko replied, "but that is not why I came to America. I wished only to visit my sister and. . . ."

"And take her back to Japan with you," Mrs. Bonnell finished the sentence for her.

"That isn't true," Flower protested.

"Don't lie to me! Go back, both of you! That's where you belong. That's where all Japanese belong. If only you had never left your country—none of you, ever. We would have been so happy. . . ." Mrs. Bonnell burst into tears and groped for a handkerchief.

Irving, by helpless grimaces and gestures, pleaded with the sisters to understand. No one knew what to say or do; they sat like puppets waiting for the master to pull the next string. In the background of the sobs that punctuated Mrs. Bonnell's tears could be heard the chirrup of crickets in the garden and from far off the drone of airplane engines in the night.

After what seemed an eternity, Mrs. Bonnell lowered her hands and stared toward the window. "What's that?" she asked.

All three strained to hear and see—there was nothing unusual.

"Do you hear them?" The woman's voice rose.

"Mother, it's only some planes from the base."

The planes were louder now. The wind was from the

90

east and the planes had to fly over the Bonnell house for a proper landing.

"Yes, planes—planes . . ." his mother repeated. "Planes—Jap planes—coming in low. They're heading for the harbor—oh, Jim! Come home, Jim! Don't stay there; they'll get you—Jim!!"

Her misty eyes saw the sisters staring at her. But they were not gardener, not tea hostess, least of all daughter-in-law—they were two Japs!

The planes skimmed the rooftop of the house; the roar of the engines muffled the distraught woman's screams as a stormy sea drowns out the cry of a lone gull. The planes went on, taking their thunder with them, and Mrs. Bonnell buried her face in the cushion next to Flower's knee. "Jim, Jim—why did they come? Why did they come?" she sobbed.

Irving knelt beside his mother and stroked her hair. His wife sat unmoved, and the lieutenant knew he would have to tell her the story he had determined she should never hear.

"Jim was my father," he began. "Dad was on board a destroyer when the planes hit Pearl Harbor. He never knew what happened." Irving paused, but his hand never ceased the gentle caressing.

"I was only one at the time. Mother was very bitter." He shrugged, and for a moment his hand slowed.

"I guess I was wrong, but I made Mother promise

91

never to tell you. I could understand how she felt, but I thought once she met you . . ." he shrugged helplessly. "Well, it didn't work."

Mrs. Bonnell straightened, gave a last sigh and wiped her eyes. "I'm glad it's out," she said. "You should never have asked me—it's been too much of a strain."

Wordlessly, Flower gazed at her. The girl rose, picked up the dried blossom her sister had given her and placed it gently in her mother-in-law's lap.

"Why?" Mrs. Bonnell asked, some of the old tension returning to her face. "Why have you always accepted my taunts in silence? It would have been so much easier to hate you, if you had only struck back. Even now you sit there calmly, as if nothing had happened; you give me a flower—why?"

Flower sighed, but her voice was filled with affection.

"In my heart I often wanted to retaliate—even to run away from you and my husband. I knew you disliked me, but try as I might I could not find out why. Now I understand and a cloud has lifted. Why should I wish to strike back at you or to leave you? It would give me no happiness, and it would dishonor the grave of my father."

"You never told me your father died," her husband said.

"I learned of his death only recently, and just this morning Miyuko gave me the details. She came here because my dying father asked her to bring me his blessing."

For a woman who believed in observing the amenities Mrs. Bonnell proved sorely lacking in sympathy. She seemed almost to relish the news as she remarked: "At least your father lived long enough to enjoy his children. My son can't even remember what his father looked like!"

Miyuko could be still no longer. Calmly, but strongly, she spoke her feelings of love and pity.

"Ever since I met you this evening I have wondered about the expression in your eyes; it reminded me of my father. My sister mentioned this to me when we were alone in the kitchen, for she recognized it also. Now I know what this likeness is. You, like our father, suffered very much in life.

"Before my sister and I were old enough to talk, Father was severely burned. He was taken to a hospital in Tokyo, and there he remained until his death. You are right when you say that we were more fortunate than your son in having our father for many years. We were permitted to visit him, and we never missed a single day. Each moment at our father's bedside was precious to us. From his burned lips we learned about the gods and about life and death. He gave us courage to face life.

"Because of his love for us, we wished to bring happiness to his heart. Flower created this happiness through her garden, and every plant she grew was destined to take its place in the vase beside our father's bed. As for me, from the time I was able to hold a bowl in my hands, I performed the tea ceremony every day in my father's hospital room; I had no desire to prepare the green tea for anyone except our father.

"After our country's defeat in the war, we were able to find life worth living—thanks to him. When my sister asked him about marrying an American, he gave her his blessing and said, 'It is good that former enemies be united by love.'

"One month ago he died in that same hospital. The doctors said he lived all those years in great pain, but he never showed it to us. Perhaps this is why we were not frightened by the darkness in his eyes. When I performed the tea ceremony this evening, for some reason the darkness in your own eyes became as warm as our father's.

"At his funeral they held a special ceremony attended by many Japanese; your American ambassador to our country came. Father was the latest person to die as a result of the atomic bomb explosion on Hiroshima."

Miyuko became silent.

Mrs. Bonnell stared at the sisters. The lines around her eyes relaxed. She picked up the dry blossom lying in her lap and lifted it slowly until it touched her lips.

4   Drive-in Desert

MAHMUT'S MOTORCYCLE COUGHED AND SPUTTERED up the steep dirt road. The mailman resigned himself to walking the rest of the way; during twenty years of delivering mail, only once had the motorcycle carried him to the top of the mountain. What a day that was to remember! The men of the village fired their rifles in salute while the women whooped, "Ya-hoo! Ya-hoo!" from the windows. No greater fanfare could have greeted the village chief returning from a victorious battle.

Mahmut knew such a day never would come again, at least not with this motorcycle. Each time the motor conked out, he was farther and farther from the village. As calmly as if he had intended to ride no farther, Mahmut slid off the cycle, pushed it to the side of the road, and leaned it against an olive tree. He unstrapped the mailbag, slung it over his shoulder, and continued up the hill on foot.

"What does it matter?" he thought. "Here on the mountain the air is cool, and one does not mind walking." Someone had suggested that the motorcycle be traded for a donkey, which could travel the mountain path just as fast and certainly farther. But Mahmut wouldn't consider it. Have some stranger see him delivering mail by donkey and write to an American newspaper about the quaint postal system in Algeria? Let the world know that even in the remotest mountain village on the edge of the Sahara Desert mail is delivered by a mailman on a motorcycle! If he had to walk a few steps, did not the mailmen in America do likewise? So he had been told by an American tourist in Algiers; in fact many covered their entire route on foot.

"Good morning, Mahmut," a villager greeted. "Any letters?"

"Nothing for you."

A letter to the village was so rare that everyone knew of its delivery before the last line could be read. Mahmut never discussed any of the letters he carried—whence they came, or from whom. He could afford to act officially aloof since few of the villagers could read; eventually the mailman was called upon to decipher the letter and to read it aloud. Occasionally he was asked to remain for dinner so that he might pen his host's reply.

Today's letter was for Mohammed Hadj, one of the elders of the village. By the time Mahmut reached his house, a crowd was following him.

"Letter for Mohammed Hadj," the mailman called.

Someone from the crowd asked, "Is it from America?"

"I don't know; I haven't looked," Mahmut replied.

Mohammed Hadj invited the mailman into his house. Since the village was little more than a large family and to enter any house was like moving from one room to another, several men from the crowd followed Mahmut inside. After all were seated on the dirt floor, the elder examined the envelope and announced, "The letter is from the oldest of my sons, Idir."

The visitors nodded their heads.

"When does he return?"

"He has not forgotten his father."

"Nor his village."

"If he continues to write as he does, he will have nothing more to tell us when he returns."

"God has blessed you, Mohammed Hadj, with such a son."

The master of the house smiled. "God also has blessed me with fields," he said, "but if I do not cultivate them they will produce only thorns. Is a son less important than a field?"

He opened the envelope with a knife, unfolded the

99

letter, handed it to the mailman and said, "Please read aloud for all of us to hear."

Mahmut cleared his throat and began.

"Beloved Father!

"I long to be with you again; to ride at your side through the desert and along the path to our village; to hear once more counsel from your lips and to be comforted by the peace in your eyes. For nearly a year I have been deprived of these joys—may God grant that I may enjoy them again someday.

"The people in America are kind. They try to make me feel at home, but there is much in their country that is different. It is hard for me to become accustomed to their ways. I wrote before that they waste enough food and water for our village to live on. This I understand better now, for they have everything in abundance. If our own olive trees were as numerous as the stars, we would also throw away the small olives that do not give enough oil to repay our efforts.

"But I cannot understand their attitude toward God. Some men in our village worried that I might forsake our Muslim religion. The danger of forsaking God altogether is greater here than is the danger of changing from one religion to another. In their day-to-day living Americans have little or nothing to remind them of their duties toward God. Once a week they sit for an hour in their churches (something like our mosques), but that is all.

"Often I find myself listening for the call of the muezzin* to remind me that I am God's servant and to summon me to prayer. But the noises that strike my ear in America arouse no thoughts of God.

"An American may tie a string around his finger to remind him to buy bread on his way home—yet he forgets! How can the thought of God become fixed in their minds when they take only one hour a week to remind themselves of him! Last week I spent an hour in a church; it did not fill the hunger in me. In the desert I could spread my rug on the ground, and the wind and the yellow sand, the red sky and dark hills, even the stork's clatter through the silence, put wings on my prayers. But in their church I could not direct my attention to the greatness of God.

"Until now I have remained faithful to the commandments you gave me. But my will is weakening—this is my reason for writing to you now. At home, if temptation arose, I could gain strength to overcome it by looking into your face. Can you not find a way to send this strength across the ocean to me? I need it.

"In our village it was easy to obey the command to guard my sexual purity until I reached the age of adulthood. Everyone else observed this commandment, so

* Muslim crier of the hour of prayer.

101

the thought of breaking it never entered my mind. *Now*, for the first time, I understand that if we do remain pure, the credit is due to the good customs handed down to us by our ancestors. In America such customs do not exist, and I have become painfully aware of their true significance.

"The Americans laugh at our customs and consider us ignorant, backward people. I confess that I began to yield to this opinion. Forgive me—I have not yet learned your ability to observe all sides of a question. Now I know why our women wear veils and cannot mingle with men except in their own families; why our women do not cut their hair and why our men wear mustaches; why our brides and grooms are never alone together until after the marriage ceremony; why all the males of our families are brought up to be responsible for protecting the females from temptation. Such customs exist among us chiefly to help us obey this commandment to guard our purity.

"I never realized before that even the simplest duties of life in our village are arranged for our moral benefit: Only a man may cultivate the olive tree, and only women may gather the olives when they fall to the ground. Only a woman may draw water from the well and carry firewood to the home, and only the arm of a man builds the well and swings the ax to cut the tree.

"In America men and women are mixed together;

they are confused as to which duties belong to the one and which to the other. Since they do not have customs such as ours to regulate their daily life, Americans— especially the young ones—are at the mercy of all kinds of temptations. And I, your son, am also. I have told you that my will is weakening. I need help badly and if it does not arrive soon, I fear I will betray you and myself.

"If Mahmut is reading this letter to you, let him write your answer immediately. Even a few words of greeting will refresh me for the journey ahead. And if God should grant that they contain the wisdom to guide me safely home, then may the blessings of a loving and obedient son be yours in your old age.

Idir"

The listeners remained silent for a few minutes after Mahmut's voice stopped, then everyone stirred and be- gan to talk excitedly. Mohammed Hadj raised his voice above the babel and invited all to remain for dinner. "First we must satisfy the needs of our bodies, then we shall reason together so Mahmut may write what is necessary for my oldest son."

Their conference lasted late into the afternoon and Mahmut was obliged to read the letter aloud several times.

"Your son was too young to leave his village," one

guest remarked. "Now he is in the wilderness; he is separated from us by an ocean. You should not have let him go."

"Remember the time Idir got lost in the desert?" Mohammed Hadj asked. "He was only seven then. All the village went to search for him—to no avail. When we returned, he was here waiting."

"God had mercy upon him," replied the guest.

The father turned his eyes heavenward. "Praise God the All-Merciful!"

After a short pause he continued: "When my son knew he was lost, he sat down on the sand and remained quiet for a long time. Then he arose and walked back to our village as if a rushing stream marked the path for him. If, at the age of seven, he could hear and follow the voice of God leading him out of the desert, why do you fear to let him out of the village when he is seventeen?"

"What is this temptation he writes about?" another guest asked. "How can we advise him when we do not know the name of the demon that torments him?"

Mohammed Hadj answered: "It is enough that Idir knows its name. My son seeks not advice, but strength to wage the battle. He has gone to America to learn what may benefit our village and our nation. Now he asks our help that he may return whole."

"What will he teach us when he returns?" Mahmut

asked. "How to break the commandments? How to change the customs given us by our ancestors?"

His host smiled. "Perhaps he will be able to teach you how to make your motorcycle obey the command to carry you to the top of our mountain." The guests laughed, and the mailman hid his embarrassment by taking a pen and paper from his satchel. He announced that he was ready to write the reply to Idir's letter.

Mohammed Hadj glanced at his visitors for approval, nodded to Mahmut and began to dictate.

"Eldest of my sons, Idir:

" 'God is most great . . . , I bear witness that there is no god except God: I bear witness that Muhammad is the Apostle of God. Come ye unto prayer. Come ye unto good. Prayer is a better thing than sleep. God is most great . . . . There is no god except God.'*

"We are not taught to read with our eyes the words of the muezzin. His call is a sound that touches our ears and stirs our hearts so that we stop what we are doing and remember only the Almighty, the Most Merciful, the Giver of Life. I am writing his call for you because you say the muezzin cannot be heard in America. If you do not hear his call, and if you do not bring yourself to

* Traditional call of the muezzin, usually made from a minaret at the appointed hours of daily prayer. (Kenneth Cragg, *The Call of The Minaret* [New York: Oxford University Press], 1956.)

prayer, why do you complain that your will is weakening? Can it be otherwise? Are the American demons more fierce than the demons of our desert? Cannot God drive them out? You must find a way to awaken the muezzin in your life.

"I do not advise you to carry your prayer cloth to school or to kneel on it before strange eyes. It is better for you to weave your thread into your host's rug so that none may be offended by you. Outwardly you must be like the lizard that blends its skin with the ground, but inwardly, you must be true to God. As a boy you were lost in the desert; after your return you told us a voice seemed to guide you back to our village. Can you be silent and hear this voice again? Perhaps it will be the muezzin for you."

Mohammed Hadj stopped speaking and stared at the ground. One of the guests broke the silence to offer advice.

"You have written wisely, Mohammed Hadj. God is truly the Source of Life and Giver of Strength. But your son's letter says that once he could overcome temptation merely by looking into your face. No doubt he is aware of God's mercy but he has written to you, not to God. Therefore I suggest that you reveal to him how he may drink again from your fountain, even in America."

"Thank you, friend of my son." Mohammed Hadj

touched his breast with the palm of his right hand. "I was silent just now because of my reflections on this same matter. Is my oldest son a jackass that he must be told to pray to God for strength?"

He nodded to the mailman, who picked up his pen and wrote as Mohammed Hadj continued:

"Without God's blessing nothing can help us, not even a letter containing all the world's wisdom. God bestows his blessing on those who draw near to him. Do not I, your father, give you my blessing whenever you ask it? Therefore listen carefully: When you are attacked by the demon urging you to break the commandment of sexual purity, picture in your mind the face of your father who loves you dearly, and speak loudly and clearly. . . ."

Mohammed Hadj stood up, raised his arms toward heaven and intoned in a deep, strong voice:

"Ya abi inzel min al-jabal oua ahdi ibnak al-mahboub min hathihi as-sahra!"

"Man, I can't wait to see Idir's face when we pick him up." Bill sat behind the wheel of his father's convertible; beside him sat his girl friend, Frill. Christened Frances, she had been nicknamed "Fran" until she began sticking to Bill like moss to a tree. A hurried "Hi, Fran, Bill," inevitably became "Hi, Fr-ill." And the name stuck.

"Excited, Margie?" Frill asked the girl in the back seat. The pretty blonde, holding her hair with both hands to protect it from the wind, made no reply. She just smiled and winked.

"Don't worry about your hair," Bill quipped. "It'll be plenty mussed up before the evening is over."

"Don't be fresh," said his date and turned again to Margie. "Every girl in school has dreamed of a date with Idir, and you're the first to have one. Aren't you thrilled?"

"Some date!" Margie answered. "He doesn't even know about it."

"Of course he knows," Bill said. "I told him I'd pick him up at nine."

"Did you tell him why?"

"To go to a movie."

"And who with?"

"I told him I might bring some friends along."

"Female friends?"

"Don't spoil it, Margie. He's like any other fish. Hold out the bait and he'll bite. Why do you think we picked you? There isn't a girl in school with more—ah—experience."

Margie bridled and tried to look indignant.

Bill laughed again. "Relax, Margie. This is Bill, remember? Save the lady bit for your old man. First we pick up Idir, then we go to the drive-in, and after that he's all yours. We won't even look in. . . ."

"I'm not sure we should go through with it," Frill interrupted.

"Baby, the guy's bashful, that's all. Maybe he never saw a girl before he came to this country. This is all part of his education. What's he, seventeen years old? How many seventeen-year-olds you know never had a date? I'm telling you, we're doing him a favor!"

"Besides," Bill added, lowering his voice to Frill, "I got a bet with some guys that when Margie gets through with Idir he won't even know what movie was playing."

The tires screeched as Bill slapped on the brakes. "Whoops—almost passed the house, be right back," he said, and jumped out of the car. He ran up the walk and in a moment returned with Idir.

"This is Frill and Margie," Bill introduced. "They wanted to see the movie, too."

"You didn't tell me . . ." Idir began softly.

"What's the difference? Hey—maybe you're short on cash? Don't worry, I know the girl at the gate."

"It's not that." Idir hesitated. "I'm not dressed properly."

"Come on, it's dark. Who can notice what you're wearing?"

"I'll just put on a tie," Idir said, and ran to the house

109

without waiting for an answer. Instead of looking for a tie he walked round and round his room. Am I lost in the desert, wandering like a newborn lamb in search of its mother? he wondered. What did I do when I was lost —long ago? Remember?

Idir sat on the stool beside his desk. His eye fell on the envelope containing his father's letter—a letter read so often that it had become as much a part of him as his heartbeat. The wave of excitement that had tossed him about flattened out into ripples. The roaring ceased, and through the stillness came the cry of the muezzin:

> God is most great. . . .
> There is no god except God.

"Blow the horn!" cried Bill, who was pacing the sidewalk impatiently. Frill reached over and honked three times. Idir bounded out of the house and walked toward them, adjusting his tie on the way.

"What movie are we going to see?" he asked.

"Movie? Oh. . . ." Bill turned and whispered to the girls. "What the heck is the name of the movie?"

The look they gave him said, "Are you kidding?"

Bill opened the rear door for Idir. "It's a surprise. You'll like it."

"Maybe a cowboy film?"

"Maybe," said Bill.

110

The movie bored Idir. It was an Italian film and he could understand little of it. He stopped watching and looked up at the stars. Usually, the lights of the city painted out the stars, but the drive-in was in darkness, and he could imagine himself on the desert—there the stars multiply right before your eyes. As he gazed upward he heard a whirring sound and overhead everything blacked out. Bill had raised the top of the convertible. There was nothing to do but watch the movie. Idir tried, but his vision was blocked by the two in front. Bills' arm was flung partway across the back of the seat, in order to accommodate Frill's head as she leaned against him.

Idir shifted his position, first to the left—he could find no opening, then to the right—he bumped into Margie. He straightened up quickly and glanced at the girl. She smiled and grasped his hand. He pulled his slowly away, but her hand followed. Could she be cold? he wondered. But the night was warm and the car was covered.

"Are you cold? Would you like to wear my jacket?" Idir asked.

"If I sit a little closer, I'll be fine," she answered and pressed against his side. Frill giggled. Bill reached up to adjust the rearview mirror.

"I don't like this movie," Idir said to Margie. "Is the next picture a cowboy film?"

111

"Close your eyes and pretend you're sleeping," Margie coaxed. Snickers came from the front seat.

She stroked Idir's neck gently with her left hand, while her right slipped under his jacket and rubbed his ribs. Her perfume drifted in circles around his head.

Idir couldn't describe the sensations pulsing through him like a warm fire. Was it paradise or was it hell? Where did all these strange new feelings come from? So pleasant—so exciting. Part of him delighted and wanted more. But a voice from within cried, "Wait! Wait! It is too early!" The face of his father flashed through his mind. Idir opened his eyes and moved forward so quickly that Margie slumped to the seat beside him. He leaned his elbows on the back of the front seat, and intoned:

"Ya abi inzel min al-jabal oua ahdi ibnak al-mahboub min hathihi as-sahra."

Bill and Frill jumped apart. "For pete's sake, what was that?" asked Bill.

Frill looked at Margie, as startled as they, and at Idir, who sat on the edge of the seat, his eyes fixed straight ahead on something she could not see.

"Are you all right, Idir?"

"Yes, I'm fine," he replied. "Why did you put the top up? Would you please put it down? It's very warm in here."

"Sure," Bill said. He winked at Margie, who seemed unusually embarrassed.

Margie moved back into her own corner. Funny, she thought, it should be an unbearable insult that a boy resisted my charms—never happened before. For the first time in my life I'm really interested in my date. What's the matter with me? No dancing? No loving? No gossip? Not even a joke?

Margie was wide awake. She had no desire to break up the evening and go home. A thousand questions were taking shape in her mind. Finally she spoke. "I'm sorry, Idir."

Idir smiled at her—a smile she might have expected from a benign grandfather, a smile she had never received before, not even from her own father. It made her feel alive and fresh and clean.

"What's the matter, Idir?" Bill asked. "Was Margie too fast for you? If you don't know what to do, watch Frill and me. Of course, we're only amateurs compared to Margie but. . . ."

"Shut your big mouth," Margie snapped.

"What do you want me to do?" Idir asked Bill.

"Don't be a goon! Are you blind? What do you think we've been doing in the front seat—watching the movie?"

"If you do not watch, why come?"

Bill laughed—Idir couldn't be serious! "You got anything against girls? You're in America now. This is the twentieth century. People grow up early here. We know what it's all about. In your country don't they teach you about the birds and the bees—about. . . ."

"About what?"

"About boys and girls—you know, getting together —love, sex, how to make babies, etc."

"Ah, yes," said Idir. "What you are referring to, I saw every day at the marketplace in my country."

Bill grinned at the girls. "I told you he's not as innocent as he looks." He turned again to Idir: "All you have to do is imagine that you're in your marketplace, in a nice dark corner, all alone with Margie, and. . . ."

Idir began to laugh. "No women are permitted in our marketplace."

"Well, what the heck kind of sex do you see there?"

"Your idea of sex is well-known even to the small children of my village. There is a parking lot in a grove of trees next to our marketplace, but instead of automobiles, we park donkeys. Sometimes hundreds of donkeys wait there to carry the goods their masters purchase. Naturally there are male and female donkeys. Their masters rejoice over our parking lot sex because their herds thereby multiply. Every one of our children knows how baby donkeys are made; most have watched the birth itself as well.

"Is this the sex you mean when you speak of birds

and bees? We learn about it even before we begin school; for us it is as natural as drinking water from the village fountain. We do not have to be told nor do we have to read books in order to know about this kind of sex."

"Then what's all the fuss," Bill asked. "Maybe you don't like Margie? Not your type? Come on, trade seats with me. You take Frill and I'll keep Margie warm."

"With longer ears and a saddle on your back, you would fit quite well in our parking lot. Our donkeys also like to change their companions at every visit to market."

It was too dark to see the color rush to Bill's face, but his silence spoke volumes.

Idir continued: "Our parents *do* teach us about sex but not about the birds and bees; we learn that merely by watching nature all around us. We are taught that the sexual act serves a great purpose in life—not merely to make babies, but to help us grow into real men, into sons of God. That is why we consider it a sacred act, more holy than any religious ceremony."

Idir paused, looked at Margie, and asked her, "How old are you?"

"Nearly sixteen."

"That means you're fifteen."

"Yes, but I'll be sixteen in a few weeks."

"For sixteen years nature has watched over your body's growth. Soon nature will leave you alone, for she

115

does not need to have you any larger. Nature does the same for the animals. But God placed a seed in us that is not in the animals, and this seed must also grow. It cannot grow automatically like your body. We must be gardeners who cultivate this seed until it bears fruit."

"Oranges or bananas?" Bill chortled.

"In your case perhaps you may never find out," Idir said shortly. "God has sent many prophets to teach us how this seed can grow. Our ancestors discovered what helps or hinders this growth, and they passed this information on to us in the form of customs and commandments. We observe a strict commandment to guard our sexual purity until we reach the age of adulthood, then and only then are we able to perform this act with reverence."

"What happens if you break the commandment?" Margie asked.

Idir replied, "My father once gave me a seedling from an olive tree. He told me to plant it in fresh fertilizer. Within a week the seedling died. We also had a full-grown olive tree that yielded a very poor crop. My father advised me to throw as much fertilizer as I could find around the base of the tree. At the next harvest, the tree produced more olives, larger and tastier, than any other tree on the mountain. Then my father said to me: 'If you have sexual relations before you have grown to be a man, it will affect you as the fertilizer affected the seedling; but if you wait until you are fully grown, you will benefit from such a relation as the tree did from the same fertilizer.' "

"You're talking crazy," Bill cried. "We're living in the twentieth century—the space age. You're not in your village—this is the modern civilized world. We don't believe in superstitious taboos anymore. All we have to do is be careful, know how far we can go and what we can get away with."

Frill agreed. "We're not doing anything wrong; we love each other. You said it's as natural as drinking water. All my friends park. What harm is there in that?"

"My ancestors must have realized that part of us wants to behave like a donkey. So they passed on customs and commandments to help us behave like humans. I cannot understand why *your* ancestors did not leave you with similar guidance. I don't blame you. You are surrounded by temptations—everyone is plotting to feed the donkey in you."

"Don't worry, we can take care of ourselves," Bill said. "These things may seem like temptations to you because you're not accustomed to them. But American kids are different. We can control ourselves."

Idir smiled. "Prove it to me. If you and Frill can sit apart for the rest of the movie, I will agree that American youth has more will power than the youth of my

117

village and doesn't need customs and commands to guide them."

Bill looked at Frill. She nodded her head, and each moved to opposite ends of the front seat.

It was downright embarrassing! What would people think—two couples in a convertible actually watching the movie? Bill's only comfort was that other couples would be too occupied with each other to notice how far apart he and Frill were.

He squirmed each time anyone walked by to the refreshment stand. Thoughts scurried as he twisted and turned:

Careful! Here comes a couple. Forget it, they're too dreamy-eyed to notice anyone in your car. Look at the sweater and pants on her! Wow! The way he's got his arm around her, you'd think they were soldered together. Damn Idir, he's spoiling my whole night!

Frill, too, was bored with the movie; her eyes and her mind roved:

What's the commotion in the next row of cars? Someone's radio is on. Listen to that beat—da-da-da-da-dummmm —da. Hey, they're dancing in the aisle over there. Don't worry, he sees them. How could he miss those red shorts on her? Wonder who the boy is? He certainly can dance. . . .

"Idir, do you mind if I talk with you?" Margie asked.

"Don't you like the movie?"

"No."

"Neither do I."

"What language was that you spoke?"

"Arabic—the language of my village."

"What did it mean?"

"What?"

"What you said when I—when I was close to you," Margie faltered.

"You will not understand."

"Please tell me."

"It means in your language, 'Father, come down from the mountain and lead the son whom you love out of this desert.' But it means a great deal more than that to me."

"Why would you ask something like that?" Margie persisted.

"I needed my father's help."

"What for?"

"You would not understand."

"Was it your own father you were speaking to?"

"Yes."

"Is he dead?"

"No, he lives in our village."

"Then why did you call to him?"

119

"I said you would not understand."

"I hardly talk to my father, even when he's in the same room with me."

"Too bad."

"Yes," she agreed sadly.

The girl sounded so bereft that Idir was moved. She looked so small—so vulnerable—huddled in her corner. Why, she's only a child, Idir thought.

"Would you like to hear about the time I got lost in the desert?" he asked, gently.

"Oh, yes! Did your father bring you home? How long were you lost? Were you hungry and thirsty? Was there a big sand storm?"

Idir smiled as the questions tumbled from Margie's lips. She leaned forward expectantly. Gone was the sad expression; instead her face was as rapt as a child waiting to be told a fairy tale.

"I was only seven, and all the village went to search for me . . ." Idir began.

Frill could hear Idir speaking in a low voice and occasionally Margie interrupting, but she couldn't distinguish their words. Frill shrugged with annoyance and again let her thoughts drift:

I don't know why Bill ever agreed to this foolish bet. And Margie, of all people, sitting back there just talking.

120

Where'd she get that angel act all of a sudden! This is the last time I'll double-date with her!

And Bill's:

Wish that girl in the next car would stop giggling. Nothing funny on the screen—what's she got to giggle about? Oh, sure. . . . Can Frill see them? Better not say anything. Ummm—Frill's perfume. Powerful stuff.

Bill and Frill glanced at each other and their eyes said, "What a wasted night—a sky full of stars laughing at us." They tried to watch the movie. But there wasn't much of a plot—just a lot of girls, scantily clad, running around. Boring? To the mind, yes; but Bill and Frill switched off their minds and began to absorb the pictures on the screen with their feelings and imaginations. Within a short time two hands crept toward each other.

Bill half-turned to face the back seat.

"Nuts to you, Idir!" he said. "I already showed you I can sit apart from Frill but I'm not going to let you spoil my whole evening. If I want to, I can take her or leave her—right now I want her."

He reached over but he didn't have to reach far—Frill was already sliding toward him.

"Thank you for proving to me the wisdom of my an-

121

cestors," Idir said. "May their teachings and command-ments remain forever on this earth!" He opened the door and began to walk away.

"Idir, wait for me!" Margie called, and jumped out after him. "You might get lost," she said.

Idir smiled at her. "Come, I know the way out of this desert," he said.

5 The Apples

(The time is shortly after V-E day—the end of World War II in Europe. The place is an American transport, docked at a port in northern Italy, discharging its military cargo and troops who will become part of the allied army of occupation. Near the dock, on the wooden platform of a bomb-damaged railroad station, American soldiers are waiting for orders. Some sit on duffel bags, still weak from the seasickness of their stormy voyage. Others stand in groups—smoking, exchanging rumors about their destination.

At one end of the platform three soldiers stand together. Duffel bags at their feet bear stencils in alphabetical order: Reginald B. Lester, Antonio F. Levalli, Samuel M. Levene. One of the three removes his shoe and sock and scrapes his bare foot on the ground.)

125

TONY: Wait'll I write my old lady. Me, Antonio Levalli, her number one bambino, rubbin' his foot on the land she ain't walked on in forty years.

REGGIE: Put on your shoe, you stink!

TONY: Whatta' ya expect after fourteen days in the belly of that ship? My old lady said, "Antonio, you get to Italy, you take off your shoes and you walk on the ground—no ground like it in the whole world!" Hell, it's as dirty as all the rest.

SAM: Put on your shoe before the captain comes.

TONY: There you go again, Sam. You know what you are? A re-incineration of my old lady!

SAM: Reincarnation.

TONY: Don't gimme no English lesson. You know what I mean. You're her spittin' image when you talk like that. Ain't you gonna tell me to button my coat so I won't catch cold?

REGGIE: Man, I'm hungry!

(*From somewhere in the crowd comes the command "Attention!" and the soldiers snap to. A captain mounts the first step of an empty train and announces: Enlisted men will be seated in the last five cars of this train; there's a long ride ahead and it's not going to be a picnic just because the war's over; no one will be per-*

mitted to disembark (for any reason) until the train reaches its destination—the Austrian Alps—tomorrow morning; a bag lunch will be provided for each man, no other food will be available until disembarkation. He orders the sergeant to get the men aboard. The men line up as the sergeant calls names and compartment numbers.)

REGGIE: What a blast! Austria! Ever hear about the girls in Austria, Tony?

TONY: My old lady won't like it.

SAM: Won't like what?

TONY: She expects me to bring home a real Italian girl.

REGGIE: So, bring home an Austrian.

TONY: They're not sloppy enough.

REGGIE: Are you planning to raise pigs?

TONY: Look, Reggie boy, you may like the kind that's pink and white, trim figure, phony hair, mascara'd eyes, and all that jazz. Me—I like 'em sloppy—big and sloppy—with somethin' inside to feed the kids.

(The three shoulder their duffel bags and board the train as the sergeant calls, "Lester, Levalli, Levene . . . compartment three, this car . . . get moving.")

REGGIE: Hey, Sarge, when do we eat? Man, I'm hungry!

127

(*Sam and Tony enter compartment three and fling their bags onto the overhead racks. Reggie enters just as the other two stretch full length on the two cushioned benches facing each other.*)

REGGIE (*to Sam*): Pull up your feet.

SAM: Why don't you sit with Tony? I'm pooped.

TONY: Nothin' doin', I got here first.

REGGIE: What gives? You want me to sit on the floor?

TONY: Why don't you take our duffel bags and string 'em out on the floor—they'll make a good mattress. Then you can lay on 'em and we can all stretch out.

SAM: Sure, good idea. I'll let you borrow my bag.

(*Reggie takes Sam's duffel bag from the rack, opens the window, and throws the bag out onto the platform. Sam springs to a standing position on the bench, but even then he is shorter than Reggie.*)

SAM: What's the idea? You better get that, Lester, or. . . .

REGGIE: Or what?

(*As Sam sticks his head out the window, the sergeant's bellow is heard: "Hey, Levene! Never mind waiting for a porter. Get out here and pick up your bag!" Sam rushes from the compartment. He returns, with the bag, to find Reggie stretched out on his bench. Sam buckles his duffel bag to the rack and eyes his two smiling roommates.)*

SAM: OK, OK, one of you pick up your feet so I can sit down.

TONY: Let's settle this fair and square. Let's throw fingers —winner gets a bench to himself.

REGGIE: No dice. We never have a chance against you.

TONY: What are you talkin' about? Ain't I taught you everythin' about this game? You know the numbers in Italian, right? You can throw fingers, right? What more d'ya want?

SAM: Yeah, but you always win. OK, we'll throw, but no callin'—Italian or anything else—just the plain old silent American version.

TONY: Lousy sports—I'm just lucky, that's all. Awright, awright, let's throw.

(Sam and Tony rise and throw fingers silently—once, twice, three times. Sam sits down. Reggie stands, throws once, and flings himself down beside Sam. Tony, whistling softly, dusts off the other bench with his handkerchief, and lies down. The door to the compartment slides open and the sergeant enters, followed by two soldiers carrying a large carton. The sergeant reaches into the carton and tosses paper bags to Sam,

Tony and Reggie. "Your dinner, gentlemen," he says, "and eat slowly; there won't be any more until we hit base in the morning." The sergeant leaves and the boys quickly open the bags.)

REGGIE: About time—I'm starving.

SAM: Ham sandwich, cheese sandwich and an apple.

REGGIE: Man, a banquet!

TONY: Is today Friday?

SAM: No, Saturday. Anyone want to trade a cheese for my ham?

REGGIE: Right here. (*They trade sandwiches.*) "Chew slowly," Sarge says. Man, I'll finish these in two bites.

TONY: First food I been able to stomach since leavin' New York. I couldn't eat the junk on ship.

SAM: That was good food. You were seasick, that's all.

REGGIE: Me, too. After the first storm I couldn't get a meal down. Now they give us two crummy sandwiches.

SAM: . . . and an apple.

TONY: Sure, for dessert!

REGGIE: Leave it to the army. I'll bet those guys in psychological warfare plan the menu. They always put a piece of dessert on it so when you start eating the dessert, you think you must have had the main meal already.

TONY: I wrote my old lady once that we get full-course dinners and she writes back, "Tell 'em not to cook the spaghetti too long, it'll get soggy."

SAM: Tony, how come you always win?

TONY: Win what?

SAM: You know—cinque, sei, tre.

TONY: Luck, I told ya.

REGGIE: Man, there's more than luck to that. We been throwing fingers since basic, and you ain't lost yet.

TONY: Special luck. The Pope blessed me.

REGGIE: Maybe I ought to change churches when I get to Hialeah again.

SAM: Come on, Tony, how do you do it?

TONY: Don't get mad if I tell?

SAM: Why should we get mad?

TONY: I win because (*pointing to Sam*) you're top-heavy and (*pointing to Reggie*) you're muscle-bound.

REGGIE: And you got rocks in the head.

131

TONY: There, you see, he's gettin' mad. I go by the feel of things. Sam, you got a good brain, but a brain ain't quick enough for this game. You try to outthink me. "How many fingers is he gonna throw?" you ask yourself. But it's too fast for thinking. By the time you make up your mind, I'm already two steps ahead.

REGGIE: He's trying to say that he always wins because he's got no brains.

TONY: Reggie boy, you belong in a circus, liftin' them barbells. Big muscles. You want something, you hold out your fist and get it. But not in this game. You throw out your fingers like you was cleanin' the guts out of a turkey.

SAM: How do you do it, Tony?

TONY: You got to have feeling. Like a cat's whiskers. You feel what's coming, how big is the crack in the fence. If the cat's like Sam, she'll take out a ruler and measure the hole and subtract that from her own size to see if she can get through. By then the dog's chewed off her tail! A cat like Reggie will close her eyes and run like a shot, thinkin' she's gonna crash through the fence even if the hole ain't big enough. Me—I got cat's whiskers that feel what's ahead. You got to have the feelin' inside.

REGGIE: I thought you feel with your hands?

132

TONY: Maybe *you* do, but the real feelin' comes from in here (*points to his chest*) without touchin' anythin'. I can feel my old lady's heart beatin' right now.

REGGIE: Only thing I ever feel inside here is hunger.

(*Sam, sandwiches eaten, takes the apple out of his bag. He studies it for a moment, polishes it on his sleeve, examines it again, then slowly puts the apple back into the bag, twists the bag shut and tosses it up onto the rack above his head.*)

SAM: I think I'll save my dessert for later.

TONY: What later? It's gettin' dark already. In an hour you'll be snorin' and when you wake up we'll be at the base.

SAM: Unless the train is late. I'm saving my apple for breakfast.

REGGIE: What makes you think the train will be late?

SAM: Don't you ever use your head? We're going up the mountains, right? That's slow enough. We just finished a war, right? You think all those bombs falling around made these tracks any stronger? This train will crawl in some places.

TONY: You ain't good for much, Sam, but you got a head on your shoulders.

133

(*Tony puts his apple back into the bag and tosses it onto the rack. Reggie does the same.*)

REGGIE: Man, I'm still hungry!

(*The three soldiers make themselves as comfortable as possible and soon fall asleep. The single light bulb in the ceiling burns dimly. Reggie, curled up in the corner, awakens; he looks quickly at the others to be sure they are asleep, lifts his hand to the rack and gropes for something. Tony awakens and sees him.*)

TONY: Whatta' ya doin'?

REGGIE: Just making sure my apple's still there.

(*Reggie's hand locates a bag. He examines the apple and appears to be about to eat it. Reluctantly he returns the apple to the bag, but instead of tossing it onto the rack again, he puts it into the pocket of his field jacket. Tony observes all this with suspicion; he rises and lifts down his own apple. Sam awakens.*)

SAM: Something wrong, Tony?

TONY: Nothin'—go back to sleep.

(*Sam sees Tony put the apple into his pocket and notices the bulge in Reggie's jacket. As he reaches for his own apple the train screeches to a halt; all three soldiers are thrown from their seats; the duffel bags fall on top of them.*)

REGGIE: God! A crash!!

(*Sam scrambles to his feet and hurries from the compartment. Reggie and Tony put the bags back up on the racks. They look out the window but can see nothing but darkness. Sam returns.*)

SAM: Some rocks fell on the track. Landslide—happens often in these mountains. Good thing the engineer spotted them in time.

TONY: Now what?

SAM: We wait until the rocks are cleared off the tracks.

TONY: Got any cards?

REGGIE: No.

TONY: How come you put the apple in your pocket?

REGGIE: No reason.

TONY: What's the matter, don't ya trust us?

REGGIE: Where's *your* apple?

TONY (*to Sam*): Old Reggie boy don't trust us!

SAM: Knock it off and go to sleep.

TONY: I'm glad the war's over, Lester. I'd hate to have you behind me with a loaded rifle.

REGGIE: You lousy wop! I'll kick you from here to the Vatican.

135

TONY: That's the closest you'll ever get to a holy place.

REGGIE: Holy like Fort Knox! At least my pocket's stuffed with my own wormy apple. I hate to tell you what's in the pocket of your Pope in his palace.

SAM: Knock it off!

TONY: Reggie boy, if you got somethin' to say against me, that's OK, but keep my religion out of it.

(*The two glare at each other. As they start to rise a shot shatters the window; all three soldiers dive for the floor.*)

REGGIE: Man, what was that?

TONY: Someone took a shot at us.

SAM: (*yelling toward door*): Hey, Sarge! Sarge! Enemy fire from outside!

TONY: Whatta' ya talkin' about? The war's over! We ain't got no more enemies!

(*From the passageway a voice yells, "Get those lights out!"*)

SAM: You heard him, Reggie.

REGGIE: Where's the switch?

SAM: You got to twist the bulb.

REGGIE: Man, that's up on the ceiling!

TONY: Don't tell me you're scared? Go put out the light!

REGGIE: Smallest guy ought to go so the enemy won't have a big target.

SAM: Go ahead, Tony. I'll kneel down and you can stand on my back.

TONY: *I'll* kneel down. You climb up.

(*They hear the sergeant roar: "Get those damn lights out!"*)

SAM: Come on, let's throw fingers.

(*The three soldiers crouch in a circle between the benches. Then one rises slowly, pushes himself up close to the wall, reaches out gingerly and twists the bulb. The compartment becomes dark, and he falls to the floor quickly.*)

(*The first light of dawn shows Tony and Reggie alone, sleeping side by side on the floor. Sam enters and shakes his comrades.*)

SAM: Wake up! Come on, it's morning.

TONY: What? Where's the enemy?

SAM (*laughing*): The *enemy* has been routed.

REGGIE: What happened?

SAM: Sarge sent some men to scout the area. All there is is a farmhouse and some old barracks on a hill. The farmer was getting in his last licks. He's been out in the sticks so long, he doesn't even know what war he's fighting.

TONY: What'd they do to him?

SAM: To an eighty-year-old grandfather? Nothing. What'd you expect? They took away his rifle and a chicken.

REGGIE: A chicken! What's she look like? Where is she?

SAM: This chicken you put in an oven and eat.

REGGIE: Man, that's even better. I'm hungry.

TONY: Why ain't we movin'?

SAM: They couldn't clear the rocks off the tracks until they found out who was shooting. We'll be starting soon.

REGGIE: How late are we?

SAM: Captain figures we'll make it by tonight if nothing else happens.

REGGIE: Come on, let's go back to that farm and get some food.

SAM: It won't work. Captain even made us give back the chicken. Farmer's got a big family and a lot of refugees have moved into the area.

REGGIE: So what?

138

THE APPLES

SAM: Well, there hasn't been much food around here lately. Captain doesn't want us to make the people angry at us.

TONY: Ain't that sweet of the old man! They been shootin' bullets at us for four years and now he doesn't want to take a chicken 'cause they might get mad at us.

SAM: I don't see any bullet holes in you, Levalli.

REGGIE: Man, I'm hungry.

TONY: "Man, I'm hungry! Man, I'm hungry!" Is that all you can say? Eat your damn apple if you're hungry.

REGGIE: I'm saving it for dessert, remember?

(*Sam takes the apple from his bag, polishes it on his sleeve, holds it in the sunlight. He smacks his lips purposefully, places the apple near his mouth as if to bite it. He watches as the others reach for theirs, continues to hold his apple and smiles.*)

SAM: How about a little bet? First man to eat his apple pays the others a buck each.

(*They put the apples back in their pockets.*)

REGGIE: Tony, you say you can feel something even when it's miles away?

TONY: Whatta' ya talkin' about?

REGGIE: You say Sam is top-heavy and I'm muscle-bound but you got it in here (*points to his chest*), and you can hear your old lady's heartbeat?

TONY: So what?

REGGIE: Well, why don't you make some kind of contact with your Pope and tell him about our predicament and ask him to whip up some sorta miracle to put some food in our hands. Nothing big—another ham sandwich is enough for me.

TONY: I told you to lay off my religion.

REGGIE: Who's picking on it? Every religion talks about making food out of nothing. Right, Sam?

SAM: What do *you* know about religion?

REGGIE: When I was a kid I learned that Jesus Christ fed about fifty thousand people on nothing—all at one sitting. Way out in the desert. And they were all hungry, just like us. He took some crumbs and he said a few words and poof—all fifty thousand had a full-course dinner.

TONY: I don't think there were that many.

REGGIE: How many then?

TONY: Maybe a couple thousand.

REGGIE: Well, man, we're only *three;* that oughta' be a cinch.

TONY: He could feed this whole army if he wanted.

REGGIE: You really believe that?

TONY: He did it once, didn't he?

REGGIE: That's what the Bible says.

TONY: That's good enough for me.

REGGIE: Great! Then why don't you ask him—for us? No problem—just three of us, and Sam only needs half a portion.

TONY: Shut up!

REGGIE: Sam, do you believe it, too?

SAM: Believe what?

REGGIE: That a lot of people can be fed when there's no food around. You know, something like pulling a rabbit out of a hat.

SAM: I don't know.

REGGIE: Don't you have anything in your religion about that?

SAM: There's a story about Moses and his followers being fed in the desert.

141

REGGIE (*to Tony*): There, you see. *Every* religion has it. Look, Tony, why don't you make contact with the Pope? Sam, you close your eyes and try to dream about Moses. Ask them how they did it.

TONY: Pope ain't ever done it.

REGGIE: Sure, but he's supposed to have the inside track with Jesus Christ. Have *him* ask.

TONY: Are you pullin' my leg?

REGGIE: Man, no! I got religion, too, don't I? As much as either of you. I'll bet I know the stories better than Tony. All I want to know is how it's possible that so many people can get fed on nothing—because, man, I'm starving right now and if I knew how, I'd do something about it.

TONY (*rising*): Know what to do about it?

REGGIE: What?

TONY: Swallow your tongue—you'll never miss it.

(*Tony hurries angrily out of the compartment.*)

SAM: Hey, Tony! Where're you going? Remember what the captain said.

(*Sam follows Tony. Reggie stretches, takes the apple from his pocket, looks at it and puts it back.*)

REGGIE: Man, I'm hungry!

(*Tony is shown opening the door leading to the rear platform of the car. He steps down into the stairwell, and gazes out onto a barren field and a small glade of trees. Sam joins him.*)

SAM: Remember what the captain said—don't get off the train.

TONY: You sound like my old lady again.

(*Tony sits on the bottom step, cups his chin in his hands and stares into space. As Sam starts to sit on the step above, the door opens and Reggie appears, stretching.*)

TONY: Gimme a cigarette.

SAM (*searches his pockets, takes out empty package*): All out.

TONY: What's that on your ear?

SAM: That's my last one.

TONY: Cheap punk!

(*Sam takes the cigarette from his ear, measures it precisely, and breaks it in half. He hands one half to Tony, who takes it without a smile or a word of thanks. Tony, in turn, takes a match from his pocket, breaks it in half and hands one half to Sam.*)

SAM: What's this?

TONY: Half a match.

SAM: You gave me the wrong half!

TONY: So what! You gave me the cork-end of the cigarette.

(*Reggie steps forward and offers Sam his lighter. Sam lights his cigarette while Tony uses the other half of the match.*)

SAM: Some lighter! Hey, Tony, look—engraved initials.

(*Sam bends forward to hand Tony the lighter. Tony lets it fall, kicks it as if by accident, then makes a half-hearted effort to recover it. The lighter falls to the ground, several feet from the train.*)

TONY: What's the matter, you got the shakes?

REGGIE: Okay, wise guy, go get it.

SAM: Who me? He dropped it!

REGGIE: One of you better get it.

TONY: Go ahead, Sam. You don't want Reggie to get mad at you.

(*Sam steps slowly down to Tony, looks around, hesitates. As he is about to jump to the ground, the train whistle blows. He hops back onto the platform. Reggie reaches into Sam's pocket, takes out the bag with the apple and throws it in the direction of the lighter.*)

SAM: What's the idea?

REGGIE: When you go for your apple, pick up my lighter on the way back.

TONY: Wait, Sam, I'll go for ya.

SAM: Go ahead.

TONY: But I might eat your apple on the way back.

SAM: Never mind, I'll get it.

(*Sam jumps down and picks up apple and lighter. Reggie and Tony laugh. Sam returns the lighter to Reggie, inspects the apple for bruises and puts it back into his pocket. All three are in the stairwell, Sam at the bottom. He kneels and bends down so that his head hangs below the train and he can see the tracks on the other side.*)

TONY: Hey, ostrich, whatta' ya doin'? You got the lighter already.

SAM: There's a blonde on the other side of the train.

REGGIE: A what?

TONY: You heard him, a blonde! Hey, Sam, ask her to crawl under the train to our side.

145

SAM: I'm not kidding. A real blonde. I saw her when I came back with the lighter.

(*Reggie steps up to the platform window, and Tony follows him. They see a small girl standing along the tracks. Tony hastens back to the stairwell, kneels beside Sam, and peers under the train.*)

TONY: *Bambina! Passare! Passare!*

SAM: What are you saying?

TONY: I'm tellin' her to come over.

SAM: How do you know she understands Italian?

TONY: I don't. She ain't comin'. You call her.

SAM: Little girl! Hey! Little girl—over here!

(*Tony lifts himself up and looks at Reggie, who is still standing at the window on the other side of the platform.*)

TONY: Hey, Reggie! Tell her to come to this side of the train.

REGGIE: I can't open the window. (*He motions with his hands to get the girl's attention.*) Go down there and come around!

(*Sam sits back on the steps and takes a small book from his pocket.*)

TONY: What's that for?

SAM: This is a German language book. Girl, girl—here it is: med-ken, med-ken. (*Sam kneels again and shouts under train.*) Hey, med-ken! Med-ken!

TONY: You sound like you're laying an egg!

SAM: She understands! She's looking under the train. Wait a minute, kid, don't go away. Stay right there. (*Sam rises, thumbs through his book.*) Go-gay-hen-zee. . . .

TONY: Tell her to go *around*.

SAM: Around—um—gay-hen-zee-um, gay-hen-zee-um, gay-hen. . . .

TONY: Don't forget that um—um.

SAM: Med-ken! Gay-hen-zee-um. Hey, down there! Gay-hen-zee-um. She's going. She understood!

TONY: You really throw that language around, Sam. Did ya study it in college?

SAM: Never knew a word until I opened the book.

TONY: No kiddin'? Say, you're great! This kid's a genius, Reggie. He picks up a language just like that. Did ya hear the way he said that um—om—oommm—just like he grew up in a barnyard here.

147

SAM: Here she comes!

(The three soldiers wave, whistle and shout to a small girl, who approaches slowly. Her blonde hair hangs in two pigtails in the rear and in bangs over her forehead. Her dress is torn. One knee-sock has fallen down to her ankle, exposing a bony leg. She hesitates, but the soldiers encourage her to come closer. She stops about ten feet from the stairwell, stands almost at attention and stares at the three. Sam finds a passage in the book and reads aloud.)

SAM: Med-ken, vee-heysen-zee?

TONY: What'd you say?

SAM: I asked what's her name. VEE-HEYSEN-ZEE?

GIRL: Ingrid.

SAM: Hear that? She understands me perfectly.

REGGIE: Go on, keep talking to her.

SAM: What do you want to know? Anything you want, I'll ask her. Anything at all.

REGGIE: Ask her if she's got an older sister.

TONY: Ask her how old she is.

SAM (*looks into book*): Vee-ahlt-zind-zee?

GIRL: *Acht.*

TONY: What'd she say?

SAM: You heard her—accchtte.

TONY: How much is that?

SAM: How do you spell it? Wait a second. Here it is—eight! Accchtte is eight. She's eight years old.

(*The train whistle blows.*)

REGGIE: Come on, let's go in. The captain will be coming.

(*Sam continues to flip the pages of his book.*)

TONY: Whatta' ya lookin' for now?

SAM: I want to say good-bye.

TONY: You mean you're givin' her the brush-off already?

SAM: We're gonna' go; didn't you hear the whistle?

TONY: That whistle's been blowin' all morning. We ain't goin' nowhere.

(*Sam continues to look in his book as Tony turns to speak to the girl.*)

TONY: *Buon giorno, bambina.*

SAM: What are you saying? She doesn't understand Italian.

TONY: She doesn't understand English either so what's the difference. (*To girl*) Why don't you pull up your stocking?

149

REGGIE: I thought you liked your women sloppy.

TONY (*to girl*): Listen, kid, when you grow up, if you ever meet a bum like this (*points to Reggie*) you'd better start runnin'.

REGGIE: She'd have to put some meat on those bones before I'd chase her.

TONY: You'd chase a scarecrow if it wore a skirt. (*He turns to girl again.*) What's the matter, kid, don't your old lady give you enough spaghetti?

SAM: You're not in the States anymore, Tony.

TONY: Sure, sure.

(*Train whistle blows.*)

REGGIE: I'm going back in.

TONY: Give the kid somethin'.

REGGIE: What?

TONY: Go ahead, give her somethin'. You ain't gonna leave without givin' her somethin'?

REGGIE: You're the one who called her over. Why don't *you* give her something?

TONY: Come on, you cheap punk.

(*Reggie reaches into his pocket grudgingly, takes out a coin and flips it to the girl. She picks it up, holds the edges of her skirt with her fingers and curtsies.*)

150

TONY: Whatta' ya give her?

REGGIE: A penny.

TONY: A penny! That musta' broke you!

REGGIE: It's all I have. It was my good luck penny, too.

TONY: Cheap punk like you needs all the luck he can get. (*He turns to Sam.*) You got somethin' for her?

SAM: You took my last cigarette.

TONY: So, you got nothin', eh, boys?

(*Tony stares at the bulges in their pockets caused by the apples.*)

REGGIE: Man, no! That apple's going right into this here stomach as soon as I get back to my seat.

SAM: Why don't you give her *your* apple, Tony?

TONY: Okay, throw fingers. Loser gives the kid the apple.

REGGIE: No more of that for me. You always win.

TONY: So what, you got a chance against Sam, ain't ya?

SAM: Wait a minute. How do you know the girl's hungry? Why don't we ask her first? Maybe she doesn't like apples?

TONY: There you go measurin' with your ruler again. Throw fingers!

(*Tony and Sam move into the shadows of the platform beside Reggie. Only their silhouettes against the window are visible as they begin to throw fingers. "Cinque, sei, quattro." There is a yell, then silence. An apple is flipped onto the ground near the girl. She retrieves it quickly as two boys run from the field toward her. The boys stand at her side and watch as she bites into the apple. They look first at the girl, then at the figures on the platform. A few moments pass and another apple is thrown out. As the boys scramble for it, a third apple lands on the ground and each child emerges with one. The train whistle blows again; the train begins to move. The children wave toward the platform.*)

(*Tony and Reggie return to their seats. Sam tarries at the window in the corridor, waving to the children.*)

SAM: Auf vee-der-sehen! Auf vee-der-sehen!

TONY: What's that mean?

SAM: Auf vee-der-sehen? Means good-bye.

TONY: What'd they say?

SAM: Who?

TONY: The people you said "off-vay-dersee" to?

SAM: The kids?

TONY: Kids—people—what's the difference!

SAM: They waved.

TONY: How about the blonde?

SAM: She just waved; couldn't say much with a mouthful of apple.

(*Tony takes the empty paper bag from his pocket, crumples it, and throws it to the floor. Sam takes his paper bag, forms its ends around his hand, puts the bag to his mouth and begins to blow. The others watch as he strikes the inflated bag with his hand—it fails to burst. He shakes the bag and begins to shape it again.*)

SAM: How come you lost, Tony?

TONY: Lost what?

SAM: Throwing fingers. How come you lost? You never lost that game before.

TONY: Hell—even the Pope can't call it right every time.

(*Sam blows up his paper bag, strikes it, but again it fails to burst.*)

TONY: You don't know nothin'. Watch me.

(*Tony picks up his bag, blows it, bursts it with a loud pop. He looks at the broken bag, then at his companions; he smiles.*)

TONY: What the hell did we do?

153

(*All three begin to laugh. Sam blows up his bag again and this time he explodes it. Their laughter increases.*)

SAM: Hey, Tony, want to know something?

TONY: What?

SAM: I'm not hungry any more.

REGGIE: Me neither.

(*Reggie blows up his paper bag. Over the pop of the bag the toot of a train whistle and the clack of the wheels on the tracks can be heard, but the loudest noise of all is the laughter of three American soldiers.*)

Conclusion

I HAVE TRIED HARD TO FOLLOW THE ADVICE OF THE Christian tinsmith in Tunis—"Learn to drink from your own well." Each chapter is an attempt to draw water from the well dug for us by Jesus Christ. If some of the central figures are non-Christian and are sketched in a favorable light, do not feel that I am "underplaying"— not pulling hard enough for—the cause of Christianity.

In "Drive-in Desert," the Muslim teen-ager is an ideal not only for Christians but for followers of his own Muslim faith as well. The qualities attributed to Idir are rarely found anywhere on earth today, but would a Christian reader feel more at ease had Idir's noble character been embodied in a representative of the Christian religion? Would we have been proud to claim him as "one of our own" and to hold him up as an example of the proper Christian attitude toward one's father and toward sex?

Because Idir is a Muslim, must we drink from the Muslim's well if we wish to be like him? On the contrary. Every ideal lifted up in this book can be attained by him who follows Jesus Christ. How will you remember the central figures in the five stories? As an African Watusi prince? As a Muslim teen-ager from the Sahara Desert? As an Orthodox refugee from Palestine? As a Japanese war bride? Or as three hungry American soldiers?

I hope not. They are human beings, and if my labeling has hindered your understanding of what I wish to say, then change their labels. Call them Christians; call them whatever you wish. They are human beings. If you would possess any of their good qualities, I repeat the advice of the tinsmith, "Drink from your own well."

Fortunately, our well is deep and does not run dry.

A WORD ABOUT THE FORMAT

The text of this book was set on the linotype in
11 point Times Roman, leaded 3 points.
Times Roman was created in 1912 for *The Times* of
London. Since then it has become
popular in all typographic fields because
of its good color, legible design,
economy of space, and excellent
reproducing qualities.

Typographic design by Margery W. Smith